the Forth
Naturalist
and Historian

Volume 29 2006

Published by the Forth Naturalist and Historian, University of Stirling – charity SCO 13270 and member of the Scottish Publishers Association. November, 2006.

ISSN 0309-7560

ISBN 1-898008-63-9

Supported by INEOS.

Cover: front– Main Street, looking west. The last white house on the left is the site of the Scotch Oven (formerly Cram's Bakery). The Crown Hotel still stands on the right and lower down a white building stands at the corner of Station Road. This was the first Dreadnought Hotel. *Callander District Heritage Society archives.*
    back– The pond at Woodland Park. *Craig Macadam.*

Printed by Meigle Colour Printers Ltd., Tweedbank Industrial Estate, Galashiels. Set in Zapf Calligraphic on Tauro 100 gsm and cover 250 gsm Silk.

THE FORTH NATURALIST AND HISTORIAN

The Forth Naturalist and Historian (FNH) is an informal enterprise of Stirling University. It was set up in 1975 by several University and Central Regional Council staff to provide a focus for interests, activities and publications of environmental, heritage and historical studies for the Forth area, comprising now local authority areas Stirling, Falkirk and Clackmannanshire.

Since then the organisation of an annual environment/heritage symposium called *Man and the Landscape* has been an important feature.

The annual *Forth Naturalist and Historian* has published numerous papers, many being authoritative and significant in their field, and includes annual reports of the weather, and of birds in the locality, plus book reviews and notes. These volumes provide a valuable successor to that basic resource *The Transactions of the Stirling Field and Archaeological Society*, 1878-1939. Four year contents/indexes are available, and selected papers are published in pamphlet form, while others are available as reprints.

In addition a 230 page book *Central Scotland – Land, Wildlife, People,* a natural history and heritage survey, was produced in 1994 and is available in the form of a CD-Rom, *Heart of Scotland's Environment* (HSE).

Other FNH and associated publications still in print include – *Mines and Minerals of the Ochils, Airthrey and Bridge of Allan, Woollen Mills of the Hillfoots, The Ochil Hills* – landscape, wildlife, heritage – an introduction with walks, *Alloa Tower and the Erskines of Mar*, and the *Lure of Loch Lomond* a journey round the shores and islands. Several of these are in association with Clackmannanshire Field Studies Society.

FNH publications are listed on the internet British Library (BLPC) and by booksellers e.g. Amazon, Bol, Barnes and Noble.

Offers of papers/notes for publication, and of presentations for symposia are ever welcome.

Honorary Secretary Marilyn Scott,
Computer Services, University of Stirling, FK9 4LA.
E-mail: mbn@stir.ac.uk
Web: http://www.fnh.stir.ac.uk

John Proctor

John Proctor longtime associated with the *Forth Naturalist and Historian* as a founder member of the Board and as a contributor died on August 25th 2006 in hospital in his home town of Accrington.

He joined the University around 1970 and rose to be professor of Botany, specialising in tropical ecology.

He had been ill for some time and eventually took early retirement because of his poor health.

He will be greatly missed by his many friends and colleagues.

FOCUS ON CALLANDER AND ITS ENVIRONS:
A PERSONAL OVERVIEW OF ITS HISTORY

Ken Dunn, Callander and District Heritage Society

Callander, as we know it today, does not have a long history – just over 200 years perhaps since the present street plan and Ancaster Square were designed and laid out to the Duke of Perth's plan of 1739. But the history of the location in the Highland borderland between the Pass of Leny and Keltie Bridge spans many hundreds of years, and geologically, thousands and millions.

Its location just south of the Highland Boundary Fault and adjacent to two significant gaps has been of primary importance to Callander's historical development. The Old Red Sandstone rocks (Pudding Stone) of the Crags to the north of the town not only give shelter from northerly blasts, but have also provided the building stone for the older properties along the Main Street. The more distant Highlands, including Ben Ledi, provided the great snowfields and glaciers which sculpted our wild and spectacular backdrop, the raison d'être of our modern tourist industry. The outwash zone of 10,000 years ago at the end of the last great Ice Age represented by the undulating hills has provided the soils for farm and forest, and more recently, valuable sand and gravel to whet the appetite of road and town builders in the industrial belt of Central Scotland.

Into this borderland environment, early man migrated and left his imprint. Such evidences have been found in many sites, for example, Neolithic homesteads and burial chambers at Auchenlaich and Ballochraggan to the east of Callander, and pre-historic forts, Caledonian or Pictish, to the west in the Pass of Leny and on Dunmore or Tarnduin Hill. All of these sites were of strategic importance, easily defended and with commanding views across the Passes into the Highland fastnesses. More recently, excavation at Claish Farm, Callander, has identified an early Neolithic farm building similar to the timber hall at Balbridie, Aberdeenshire, and dated between 3,000 and 4,000 BC.

The Romans set up temporary camps and forts along a line from Drymen, via the Lake of Menteith, to Callander and north-eastwards to Comrie. The camp and fort at Callander was situated at Bochastle, and it is thought to have been a glen-blocking fort to contain the Caledonian tribes, and prevent flank attacks on the main thrust of the Romans northwards from Stirling through Ardoch and beyond towards Perth and the Highlands. This fort lies between the two rivers issuing from Loch Lubnaig and Loch Vennacher. It was Agricolan in age, and didn't last for many years beyond 100 A.D.

The first missionary influence came from Columba's disciples on Iona. One such, St. Kessog, had mission stations at Luss and Strathblane, and tradition has it that he had a preaching station in Callander on the mount known locally as *Tom na Chessaig* (Hill of Kessog). In later years, this was followed by a Celtic foundation at Kilmahog (Cell of St. Luag or Chug), a Culdee sect of the Columban church.

Later, in the 13th century, the Augustinian Canons of Inchmahome on the Lake of Menteith, established a small chapel at Little Leny, situated on a small mound near the meeting of the rivers Leny and Vennacher. In time, both foundations and the pre-Reformation church in Callander merged, and in about 1238 were brought into the Bishopric of Dunblane. The early pre-Reformation Church was sited in what is now the old grave-yard adjacent to *Tom na Chessaig.*

As in many rural parishes in Scotland, the Reformation was a slow and gradual process of change from Episcopacy to Presbyterianism. There were problems finding ministers with the requisite qualifications to preach and teach in the Gaelic, and some didn't stay long. Others, as at Kilmahog, continued for many years quite acceptably performing the rites of the Episcopalian service. Callander Parish was now in the Presbytery of Dunblane, but sufficiently distant to go its own way – no doubt leading to many problems and disputes!

Up to the end of the 16th century, the lands around Callander belonged to the Livingstones of Callendar Park near Falkirk. They had a Tower House or Keep on the south bank of the Teith beside the former Manse. From then on, the land changed hands and became part of the Drummond estates of the Duke of Perth. In 1625 a hunting lodge was built at the "Roman Camp" – not at Bochastle, but on the site of the now prestigious hotel of that name – just across the river from the Livingstone's Tower House.

Callander's location between Highland and Lowland would seem to be parallelled to some extent by its changed estate ownership – from the lowland Livingstone family to the Drummond family with its Highland connections and allegiances, especially its strong Jacobite connection.

At the time of the 1745 rebellion, Callander and district was part of the Duke of Perth's estate and supported Prince Charles Edward Stuart. After the Battle of Culloden in 1746, the Estate was forfeited and taken over by government-appointed Commissioners who were charged with running the estate and making improvements – and much else.

Callander was fortunate. The Duke of Perth had drawn up a plan in 1739, the first and oldest plan for a new town in Scotland. The 'Enlightenment' came early to Callander! This plan was adopted by the Commissioners and the Square and wide Main Street were laid out in the 1770s.

In 1772-73, the Parish Church was moved from its original site beside the river to the north side of the new Square, later to be called Ancaster Square after the successor to the Duke of Perth, the Earl of Ancaster. This move took place during the Reverend Dr. James Robertson's ministry. Dr. Robertson was 'the man for the time' and deserves special mention at the close of this period of Callander's history.

The Reverend Dr. James Robertson had many qualities apart from his distinguished ministry. He wrote many original papers and books on a great variety of topics, including *A General View of the Agriculture of the County of Perth,* and his eminent contribution to the First Statistical Account of the Parish of Callander in 1791. For the time, both were enlightened insights into the work and life of rural folk in all walks of life. He also made sound suggestions for the improvement of farming and industry in the Parish. For example, mentioning the use of lime for soil improvement, improving stock breeds and new methods of land tenure, as well as having an interest in the establishment of small-scale spinning and weaving industries. He also advocated better roads and new bridges, not only along the most used routes of the time, but in the future when there would be a good road from Callander via Glenartney to Comrie – not yet implemented!

Dr. Robertson's influence on the future of Callander was indeed wide-ranging, but no more so than in the growth of the tourist industry. His descriptions of the Trossachs scenery in the Statistical Account would adorn the best of tourist guide books. They are the forerunner of Scott's descriptions in *The Lady of the Lake.* There seems no doubt that Scott would have read Robertson's account, and certainly the Wordsworths had, prior to their first visit to this enchanted place in the early 1800s – some years before the *The Lady of the Lake* was published in 1810.

Growth and Settlement

It was also during Dr. Robertson's long ministry in Callander that the distribution of the Parish population was going through a radical change. Subsistence farming with cattle and crops in the adjacent glens was giving way to extensive sheep farms, and families were settling in the 'new' town and its environs, engaging in a variety of trades, including spinning and weaving, merchandising, shoemaking and tailoring.

Also, as in other highland settlements, after the Seven Years War, a Soldiers' Settlement was established in an area which is now part of the Golf Course. The Highland Borderland situation of Callander was well-placed to be the centre of a thriving trade between Highlands and Lowlands, and the man for the time was Donald McLaren, 'the Banker'. He built a thriving trade transporting wool, timber and other highland products to the industrial lowlands, and as a return cargo manufactures and imports from the growing Forth and Clyde industrial belt.

At the same time, one of the drove routes from the north west Highlands came through Callander establishing an annual fair at Cockhill which continued into the early 20th century. These fascinating times and associated characters are beautifully described in James Macdonald's book *Character Sketches of Old Callander,* originally published in 1938.

Beginning of Tourism

As stated earlier, poets and other literary figures were discovering the Trossachs area in the 1790s and early 1800s, but there is no doubt that Sir Walter

Scott's works, particularly *The Lady of the Lake* published in 1810, and the novel *Rob Roy*, started the ever-growing stream of horse drawn coaches from the south leading to increasing numbers of visitors keen to explore and experience the highland fastnesses hitherto looked upon as forbidding and uninviting.

As the century progressed, and roads and means of transport improved, Callander and the Trossachs became ever more popular with the affluent middle classes from the industrial belt of Central Scotland and from the South.

"The opening of the railway produced a revolution in the village" – so said James Macdonald in his excellent book *Character Sketches of Old Callander* – referring to the Dunblane & Callander Railway which arrived in Callander in 1858. A year later, Queen Victoria and Albert first drove through the village to open the Glasgow Waterworks at Loch Katrine, and ten years on in her Journal she describes Callander as containing "a few good houses and many poor ones". But no doubt this was a turning point for Callander. Houses were extended and improved along the Main Street, new Hotels established, and trades and shops flourished to cater for the new demand. Large villas were built at the west end, known as The Feus, to cater for family holidays during the summer months, the railway providing the link to the central industrial belt. As the railway progressed up country to Oban and Fort William, Callander was well placed as a tourist centre, especially popular was the circular tour from Glasgow via Stirling to Callander and onward to Loch Katrine and Loch Lomond and back to Glasgow, using road, rail and steamer transport. It was also at this time that Callander became a Burgh with its own provost and Town Councilors (1866). Many citizens gave outstanding service to the community during this period of Burgh status, which ended in 1975 with regionalisation under Stirling and Central Region. During the latter part of this period Callander's tourist industry flourished, based mainly on cheap public transport, coach tours, the railway till 1965, and increasing private car ownership – this was the boom bed and breakfast era, still operational but now being overtaken to an extent by self-catering and activity holidays.

Callander as an Educational Centre

The foundation of modern education at all levels was mainly a product of the Free Church School established in 1849. It was Donald McLaren, 'the Banker', who provided the land and most of the money for building the Free Church after the Disruption in the Church of Scotland in 1843. The Free Church Hall built in 1849 provided primary and secondary education to university entrance standard, and was in effect a forerunner of the McLaren High School, endowed by the McLaren Trust, and founded in 1892. Donald McLaren's vision was to provide free primary and secondary education for all children living in the West Perthshire area and to ensure that text books were available no matter the financial circumstances of the families. Although Donald died in 1854, his wishes were carried out and put into effect by the McLaren Educational Trust, under the able leadership of figures such as Daniel MacEwen, founder of the famous Scottish grocery chain. Today, with a staff of over 50 and renowned for its academic and social standards, McLaren High continues to play a very important part in the life of the Callander district.

More recently, in the late 1990s, as a result of local fund raising and grants, the McLaren Leisure Centre has been built in the school grounds, and provides modern sports facilities, including a games hall, swimming pool, indoor bowls, all-weather tennis courts etc., available for the school, the general public and visitors to the area.

Callander and district owes a large debt of gratitude to these early pioneers, but also to the more recent fund raisers and volunteers who have continued the tradition of local service and foresight for the benefit of the community.

Local Government Changes

Callander had a Town Council with its own Provost and officials from 1866 until 1975 under Perth County. Gone are the days of Callander Town Council and its local accountability and civic pride. Today, Callander is part of the Stirling Council area, predominantly focused on Stirling's new city status. The rural aspect of the town and its Perthshire highland heritage has been lost in a much more centralised bureaucracy. One can but speculate on the future of many such rural communities as their identities become submerged by urban centralisation.

Further Reading Sources

Character Sketches of Old Callander – James Macdonald; Jamieson & Munro, Stirling, 1938.

Callander through the Ages – Alastair Thompson; Callander Printers, 1985.

First Statistical Account, Parish of Callander (Robertson) 1791.

The Callander and Oban Railway – John Thomas; David & Charles, 1990.

The Trossachs in Literature and Tradition – Rev. Wm. Wilson, 1908.

British Regional Geology – The Grampian Highlands – 3rd Edition, HMSO 1966.

Geology of the Stirling District, Geological Survey Scotland – HMSO 1970.

First Generations, the Stirling Area from Neolithic to Roman Times – Lorna Main, Stirling Council, 2001.

Jacobite estates of the Forty-Five – Annette M Smith; John Donald, 1982.

BOOK REVIEWS

Walk of the Week and **Walk of the Week 2**. Peter Evans. Mercat Press, Edinburgh. £8.99.
Each book contains 52 walks ranging from the easy to more demanding treks. Walks are spread throughout Scotland with only a limited local focus. The information on each walk combines folklore and history to add extra interest.
Not to be overlooked are the charming illustrations provided by Glen McBeth.

Guide to Rural Scotland. James Gracie. Travel Publishing. £11.99.
A collection of travel guides listing what to see, do and where to stay on ten journeys in Scotland.

Geodiversity: Valuing and Conserving Abiotic Nature. Murray Gray. Wiley.
Since the UN Convention on Biodiversity was signed, attention has been focused on protecting and enhancing biological diversity. However, this does not include the rocks, landforms and processes that form the physical elements of our own environment. These elements have their own diversity – a geodiversity. This is the first book to focus specifically on the geodiversity of the planet and the threats to this diversity, to explain the value of inanimate nature and to assess the approaches that should be taken to conserve it.
This book is available in Stirling University Library.

Wildlife Ecology, Conservation and Management. A.R.E. Sinclair, J.M. Fryxell and G. Caughley. 2nd edn. Blackwell.
This extensively revised edition of *Wildlife Ecology, Conservation & Management* provides a succinct and clear introduction to general ecological principles, and then goes on to show how those principles can be applied to wildlife management and conservation.
The book is appropriate to both undergraduate and graduate classes in applied ecology, conservation and natural resource management. It will also be valuable to professional wildlife biologists in developing their research and management.
It is available in Stirling University Library.

'Look Aboot Ye'.
A Clackmannanshire Ramblers' booklet of walks within 30 miles of Alloa. A selection of graded walks from 4 to 9 miles in length on circular routes.
Price £3 available from libraries and visitor centres at Gartmorn Dam and Mill Trail, Alva.
All profits will be donated to the Ochils Mountain Rescue Service.

Barry Buddon – A Major Scottish Sand Dune System. Colin R. Mcleod. The Scottish Naturalist 2005, Vol 117.
Barry Buddon peninsula on the north shore of the Firth of Forth is the most important sand dune system surviving in a near natural condition in the UK. In part its survival was due to its use as an army training ground for more than a century. It describes the natural history and human history and the way in which, even in a near natural environment, they become closely inter-twined.
The 20 chapters cover almost every aspect of climate, wildlife, conservation, geology, land use and other human activities.

THE STIRLING HEADS AND THE SMITH PANELS
Michael Bath

In 1926 an article in *Transactions of the Stirling Natural History and Archaeological Society* offered one of the clearest provenance records one could wish for concerning a museum exhibit.[1] At a meeting of Stirling Town Council in 1876, we are told, Provost Christie informed councillors that he had spent £19 on a set of carved wooden panels at a sale of the effects of the late Miss Lucas of Marieville House, Upper Bridge Street. These panels were carved with medallion heads similar to the famous Stirling Heads, of which the Council had formerly purchased and presented a dozen examples to the trustees of the Smith Institute when it had opened just two years earlier in 1874. The panels owned by Miss Lucas were believed to have formed part of the wainscot panelling of the palace, and when bought by her had all been mounted in a single frame. The Provost thought it would be appropriate for the corporation to reimburse him the £19 he had spent, and to make a further gift to the Smith Institute, though if they declined he would be happy to keep the panels for himself: 'He thought they were a very good bargain; in fact similar work could not be got under £5 per head, and if the Council did not want them he would be glad to become the real as he was the nominal purchaser' (p.169). The Provost thought it 'extremely likely' that the palace walls were wainscoted, indeed 'He had in his hand a portion of the frame in which the heads were placed when Mr Lucas got them, and he believed it was part of the wainscoting of the palace walls' (p.169). Councillors found the Provost's case persuasive, and authorised the corporation to 'purchase them, and present them to the Smith Institute for preservation'.

The sixteen panels that Provost Christie bought in 1876 from the estate of Miss Lucas remain one of the present Smith Gallery's most prized exibits, and the belief that these are wainscot panelling from Stirling Castle has passed into virtually all the extant literature describing them.[2] Indeed the provenance seemed good enough for us to seriously consider reinstating such panelling in the refurbished palace apartments which Historic Scotland is currently designing at Stirling. As a member of the academic team advising on this, however, I have to say that I am quite certain that the Smith Panels were never wainscot panelling and I have some doubt, despite Mr Lucas's testimony, as to whether they really originated in the palace. I hope, in this article, to explain why.

Medallion roundels became a very fashionable feature of renaissance decoration in the applied arts, where they figure on innumerable pieces of carved woodwork, stonework, coffered ceilings, painted friezes, metalwork and even ceramics – many Italian, French, Netherlandic, Spanish and English as well as Scottish examples survive. Originating in the late-medieval revival of classical medals, they become in the early sixteenth century a sure sign of the arrival of an Italianate, neoclassical renaissance. James V not only had some of the most inventive and vigorously carved examples on the ceiling of his Presence Chamber at Stirling, but in 1539 he also had similar medallions carved on the external stonework of his new palace at Falkland, where they can still be seen. Imperial medals feature both emperors and empresses, and medallions based on them will often, as with the Stirling Heads, include both male and female figures, either in classical or in modern attire. That combination of male and female profiles seems to have led to a fashion for using such medallions on domestic furniture, where they would be appropriate as wedding presents or signs of conjugal affection. On such furniture they no longer look like Roman emperors but more like real people, though they seldom show actual portraits of their owners as far as one can tell.

One of the most common types of domestic furniture to have used such medallion roundels, from about the mid-sixteenth century onwards, were the large clothes presses (armoires) in which husband and/or wife stored their clothing. Numerous examples of these have survived on which the large double doors consist of rectangular panels carved with medallion heads, usually with a bit of added arabesque work. It is an invariable rule with such clothes presses that there are eight panels on each door featuring four confronting roundels of male and female faces. Their carvers, and owners, evidently delighted in the varied expression, headdress and costume detail of such figures. It is, I suggest, an absolutely safe bet whenever one finds a set of sixteen panels with medallions comprising eight male and eight female profiles that they originated on such a clothes press. All one need do to test this wager is to take the measurements, which are likely to be around 25 cm x 30 cm, and to check that at least eight of the male heads look one way, and eight of the females look the other. They can then confront each other on each door in domestic pairings, if not necessarily in marital bliss.

This is indeed the case with the Smith Heads, as can be seen from the photograph of them that appeared in *Proceedings of the Society of Antiquaries of Scotland (PSAS)* in 1927 (Figure 1). James Richardson, author of the article on Unrecorded Scottish Woodcarvings, shows them in confronting pairs, inserted into a single frame – which he has sketched in pencil. He does not give his reasons for illustrating them in this way, and although his single frame should certainly be cut in half to create two armoire doors, his putative pairings show how readily the Smith heads can be grouped in this way. This is exactly how such medallion heads are mounted on such surviving examples as the 'Flemish' clothes press now in Glasgow's Burrell Collection, or the 'Queen Mary Cabinet' in the National Museum of Scotland – so called from the unverified belief that it once belonged to Mary Queen of Scots – and on numerous further examples (Figure 2).[3] We should not assume that the 'frame' which is described as holding the Smith Panels when they were removed from Stirling Castle necessarily took this form, for although Richardson notes that, when owned by Miss Lucas, the panels 'were still in their frame' (p.403), Joseph McNaughton records Provost Christie as saying, 'The reason the heads were taken out of the frame was because Miss Lucas objected to such a big thing coming into the house, and Mr Lucas sawed or cut the wainscoting' (p.169). Thus although we are told that the Provost believed he 'had in his hand a portion of the frame in which the heads were placed when Mr Lucas got them', we have only Lucas's own testimony that, when removed from the Castle, they were in a single frame. Of the shape and size of this 'frame' we learn nothing, and of Richardson's putative reconstruction we can only say that it is conjectural, if suggestive. His *PSAS* illustration certainly shows how the heads might be grouped in confronting male-female pairs, but it should not be taken as evidence that all sixteen were ever thus mounted in a single frame, or that such a mounting ever formed part of some lost wainscot panelling that once covered the walls of the royal palace in Stirling. Lucas, who had sawed up the frame more than fifty years before Richardson wrote his *PSAS* article, would still doubtless have been anxious to convince Stirling corporation that the panels had indeed come from the Palace. They may well have done, but we have only his word for it, and the idea that they were part of its fixed wainscot panelling rather than from a piece of moveable furniture would have been crucial to the sale.

Medallion roundels certainly feature on sixteenth-century wall panelling and in Britain can still be seen at Speke Hall, Lancashire, or at Temple Newsam, Leeds, where it is associated with linenfold panelling from Bretton Hall, Yorkshire, reputed to date from the 1530s. Still in England, the Waltham Abbey panels, featuring the Tudor rose, portcullis, and pomegranate badge of Catherine of Aragon, probably came from a house in Green Yard, Waltham Abbey, and were moved to the Victoria and Albert Museum in 1899 shortly before the house was destroyed by fire.[4] Such panelling is also found in Scotland, where sixteen panels reputed to have come from the so-called 'Guise Palace' in Edinburgh are now on display in the National Museum of Scotland. However these also comprise eight left-facing and eight right-facing profiles: the size of the panels, 21 cm x 31 cm, and their number suggest that they almost certainly originated not as fixed panelling on the walls of an apartment but rather as part of a carved clothes-press or *armoire*. When such pieces of large, moveable furniture became unfashionable or were replaced it was most likely to be the door panels with their carved heads that would have been preserved or recycled, which might explain why comparatively large numbers of them have survived as detached panels. It was quite natural for nineteenth-century antiquarian collectors to assume that these were antique wainscot carvings, and their new owners, such as Sir William Burrell at Hutton Castle or the Earl of Breadalbane at Taymouth would then be only too pleased to stick them on the walls of their neo-baronialised houses. This is not to say that the Smith Panels, with their engaging medallion roundels, may not have a good Scottish, or indeed Stirling, provenance. Richardson's examples of Unrecorded Scottish Wood Carvings do indeed include several further examples, for which he claims a Stirling provenance, and these can quite easily be supplemented with further Scottish examples.[5] But when such panels have become detached from their original settings it can be very difficult, if not impossible, to say what type of furniture they originally decorated, and it was only the growing celebrity of the famous Stirling Heads which led writers and collectors towards the end of the nineteenth century to assign any and every example they had recovered or identified to Stirling.[6] The time has surely come for us to query and test that assumption.

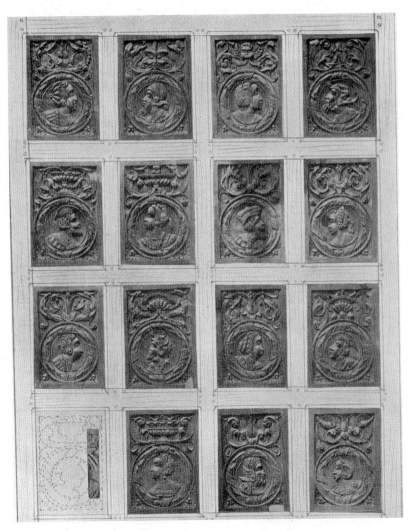

Figure 1 The Smith Panels as illustrated by James Richardson in 1927 in *Proceedings of the Society of Antiquaries of Scotland*, LX p.402, when Richardson was curator of the Museum of Antiquities; his reasons for illustrating the panels disposed and framed in this way are unclear.

Figure 2 National Museum of Scotland 'Queen Mary Cabinet' showing the typical way of mounting panels of medallion heads on *armoires* in 8 x 8 male-female pairs; the provenance of this exhibit remains obscure and it may have no real connection with Queen Mary or with Stirling.

---

[1] Joseph McNaughton, The Stirling Heads, *Transactions* (1924-25), pp.166-71. There had been an earlier article by J.S. Fleming on Sixteen Carved Panels in the Smith Institute in the same journal in 1921, pp.14-17.

[2] Eg RCAHMS *Stirlingshire* 2: 400.

[3] See for instance the 'Flemish' clothes press illustrated in Victor Chinnery, *Oak Furniture: The British Tradition* (Woodbridge, 1979), fig. 4:22.

[4] Anon, *The Panelled Rooms: The Waltham Abbey Room*, V&A booklet, 1924.

[5] These include the National Museum of Scotland's sixteenth-century 'Pittenweem Cabinet', its 'Guise Palace' door, and the carved oak door from Water Lane, Leith. Two interesting medallion panels from Killochan Castle, Ayrshire, are now in Loudon Hall, Ayrshire.

[6] For instance the National Museum's 'Queen Mary Cabinet' whose ascription to Mary is not supported by any clear archival evidence.

BOOK REVIEWS

Stirling Council Woodland Access Guide
Thirty-eight mostly well known walks within the Council area, both short and long, are briefly described with a note on transport and parking facilities.

Obtainable from libraries and tourist offices.

The Flora of Perthshire. Francis Buchan White 1898. Republished E P Publishing 1978. 404pp.
A copy has been obtained by Stirling University Library.

Nature, Landscape and People since the Second World War. ed. T.C. Smout 2001 Tuckwell Press. 240pp. ISBN 8632 147.7 Now in paperback £3.99.
First published in 1999 as a collection of papers from a conference to celebrate the 1949 National Parks and Access to the Countryside Act.

It includes consideration of prospects for nature conservation and rural recreation in the 21st century.

Birds' Egg Collections and Local Ornithology, a Case Study. Martin Limbert. Perigrine Books. Leeds I.S18 5JS. 150 copies only at £25 + £3 p&p. 65pp.
Explaining the possibility that museum egg collections maybe a valuable source of past bird breeding records.

Scotland's Environment: the Future. ed. George Holmes and Roger Crofts Tuckwell Press. 2000. 150pp. ISBN 1 8632 162 0.

THE MACFARLANE MUSEUM OF NATURAL HISTORY, CONEYHILL

J. Malcolm Allan

John Macfarlane of Coneyhill is a neglected figure in the history of Stirling, where he was born in 1785, and in the study of natural history in Scotland. In the mid-nineteenth century he had a high profile in both fields and his strident opinions were made known even after his death at Bridge of Allan in 1868. He is buried in the Holy Rude cemetery but scant traces of his legacy can be traced for what they were. He is a mere shadow in the background of his internationally famous grandson the pioneer oceanographer Sir John Murray. No longer is there a Macfarlane Street or a Macfarlane Terrace in Bridge of Allan and properties he built are not identified with his name. The Macfarlane Museum of Natural History, the pride of his old age and his intended monument, no longer exists.

The Stirling of his youth was a textile town as well as a garrison. He made a career and substantial fortune once he left the town for Glasgow and Manchester as a textile designer, producer and merchant. He had a strong entrepreneurial streak and promoted many ideas before his time while speculating also in the new gas and railway developments and in property. He is credited with moving the commercial heart of Manchester out of the congested mediaeval centre by building substantial warehouses which he then leased to other merchants. They remain there with a new lease of life as Manchester's Merchant City clubs and apartments a century and a half later.

While in Manchester he was in the van of the new organizations for knowledge, the Mechanics Institute, the Manchester Literary and Philosophical Society and other worthy bodies which broadened his fertile imagination far beyond that of being a 'Scotch commission agent'. He still held his native town in esteem and endeavoured to enlighten a disinterested Stirling Town council. He proposed a canal from Dunmore to an enlarged Stirling harbour and a canal on to Balloch in 1835, a school of design for which he commissioned plaster casts of antique statuary in 1843, a free public library, a reading room and gondolas on the Forth from the Rowing Club for which he provided a cup and a boat, all before his retiral from Manchester about 1845.

In Manchester he had formed a lasting friendship with fellow Scot and contemporary Captain Thomas Brown, an ardent naturalist and author of textbooks on natural history and taxidermy, who in 1838 became Curator of the Manchester Natural History Society. It seems that Macfarlane's interest was caught then but it was not until later it developed into a passion. On retirement he returned North and settled in Bridge of Allan. He leased and later bought the small estate of Coneyhill from his cousin, Major John Henderson, the laird of Westerton and feudal superior of the village. He lived first in Ivy Lodge, the renamed House of Coneyhill now called the Old Manor, which he improved and extended. Speculative building continued in his retirement in his own lands. He built a row of workmen's cottages and what is now Coneyhill Road with several large villas which he then rented out. His largest and most ambitious building was to be a three storey museum on Macfarlane Terrace created at the top of his new Coneyhill Road and begun when he was already 75.

The building and its contents would have been quite forgotten were it not for the chance discovery of 'Macfarlane's Letter Book No. 2' by Dr. Margaret Deacon of the Southampton Oceanography Centre among the archives of Sir John Murray at the Natural History Museum in London a few years ago. It covers the period November 1860 to April 1863 when, as a teenager, Murray became Curator to his grandfather. Murray, after the death of his father, had been brought over from Canada to attend Stirling High School for a year and to live with and be directed in life by his grandfather. The Dr W.H. Welsh Educational and Historical Trust for Bridge of Allan had a microfilm made of the letter book and this is now in Stirling Archives. As it is No. 2 then there must have been earlier correspondence by Macfarlane and maybe a later one since he lived to 1868. Among his disputes over the Wallace Monument, the Stirling Free Library, the Rowing Club and Stirling Council the main theme is a record of his building of his museum and his purchases before it opened and in its first two years.

It is known that the teenage Murray made a collection of the flora and natural history of the area and showed aptitude for the sciences while at Stirling High School. There is speculation that Macfarlane accelerated his own collecting and building to provide a career for his grandson as curator of a grand design: Scotland's Natural History Museum. The collecting was not random but by species and scientifically based with constant recourse to Captain Brown at Manchester Natural History Society. Macfarlane intended it to be the largest such museum after London and to rival an Edinburgh University collection held in their Department of Natural History. This was later subsumed into the new National Museum of Science and Arts for Scotland being planned around this time. Captain Brown had made purchases for Edinburgh before he went off to be curator in Manchester in 1838 and knew its scope. Macfarlane appears to have been collecting natural history books to support the physical exhibits from at least 1854 so his animal and birds buying may date earlier. He was no stranger to obsessive collecting. The plaster sculptures, rejected by Stirling Council, along with other curiosities had been exhibited in a hall in Bridge of Allan village, opposite the Westerton Arms, to entertain and enlighten visitors to the spa since 1846.

The rapid expansion of exploration in the mid-Victorian period constantly revealed new species of birds and animals from various continents. In such pre-David Attenborough days there were only crude wood or steel engravings as illustrations in books and periodicals, usually uncoloured, but the advance of taxidermy made it possible for Macfarlane to add to his other exhibits. His cousin, Major Henderson, a man of related enthusiasms and entrepreneurial bent, was keen to have attractions for the developing spa particularly if he could charge for viewing.

The hall, built in the village by Henderson, became too small and Macfarlane was living on his own estate from 1848 so he eventually decided to build his own halls and charge his own fees for entry. It all coincided with his idea to build the row of cottages and villas thus extending his properties into a Bridge of Allan East or Coney Hill Village around his own house. The main village did not extend much beyond Mine Road which was cut through the Lower Westerton Wood in 1844 as main access to the spa above. The museum he now planned was a plain three storey factory-type building on this level. It was on an old raised beach to form a terrace and is now occupied by a very modern house below Logie Aston House on Kenilworth Road. It looked over the carse, his cottages, Mount Hope and his own new house Edgehill opposite on Coneyhill Road. He let out the original Coneyhill/Ivy Lodge and by 1863 was building a new Coneyhill House on the high part of his estate entered from 'the Eagle Gates' already erected as a feature to his grounds before 1861 and which also probably served as entrance to the museum.

The first copied letter, dated 8 November 1860, to Captain Thomas Brown is quite informative about his operations. He had bought skins from J.C. Stevens of London, an auctioneer and taxidermy dealer used by Brown as well, and suggests the cheapest way to send bulk items from London was by sea to

Eagle Gates entrance to the Macfarlane Museum of Natural History, now the entrance to Coneyhill House, Kenilworth Road, built 1863.

Grangemouth as now there was a new railway link to Stirling and Bridge of Allan. As the story unfolds one wonders how the porters at Bridge of Allan station reacted to large crates of stuffed specimens or boxes of very dead ones requiring skinning which then had to be carted the length of the village to Coneyhill.

The museum building was already occupied and even receiving visitors, 'Stirling of Keir accompanied by Lord John Manners. They had no conception that so large a collection of Natural History existed in this part of the world.' The third storey was about finished and roofing to start the next week. He went on to discuss a tiger skin he wanted from Stevens and his need for flying squirrels, Australian pelican, a kangaroo and butterflies 'if got cheap'. He always states carefully the specimen's sex he needed, the gaps in genera he wished to fill and the condition. Skins were to be sent first to Brown in Manchester for stuffing but cased pieces came direct.

The building progressed slowly because of the weather and delays by the glazier up to Christmas. By January 1861 he was busy furnishing the interior and had no place to store extra specimens which were not in cases. By April he reported to Brown that more than 100 had signed their names in the visitor's book so it seems the major collection was open as soon as the season for spa tourists began in March 1861. Next month there was a decision on a steam pipe heating system, commenced in June. Up to this time it appears to have been called Coney Hill Institution but in July new labels were ordered for books which read *The Macfarlane Museum of Natural History and Gallery of Casts and Paintings*. The latter he bought as job lots, refusing to pay more than £5 for them as the public did not know quality or the difference in his estimation. All the time he was adding specimens and even building an extension until in May 1862 he had to refuse purchase of a set of Gould's Birds of Asia as 'I have overdone my funds in the building works etc. I have been erecting lately and, for the present, I have to suspend the building of the New Museum Additional and I have to pause …'. In addition to extending the museum, which was to include a reading room and the library of natural history books, there was a cottage for the boiler man/janitor. This was on Macfarlane Terrace, the name given to the old shore line ledge which began at Coneyhill Road and went below Logie Aston and Arrochar Villa (later manse for Chalmers Free Church) to come up on Kenilworth Road near the Chalton Road junction at Lea Cottage.

It was not the building that was important but the contents. Their purchase by correspondence, with Macfarlane's reports to Brown give an idea of the scope since no collections catalogue is known to exist. There are eleven letters to J.C. Stevens, the auctioneer of skins and taxidermy at King Street, Covent Garden and no less than fifty four to Captain Brown about the collection, work on displays and the deliveries of specimens. In addition he wrote to menagerie owners to take newly dead beasts off their hands at a small cost. In 1863 he was in dispute with Manders Menagerie, Lothian Road, Edinburgh over the state of a lion too decayed to skin and he sent it back. He sent his grandson to Perth to bargain over a giraffe that died there and bought it for 15 guineas. At one point he tried to do a deal with London Zoo to get the first refusal on carcases after the London Natural History Museum made their choice. It was not productive since a year later he comments to Brown 'The Zoological Gardens, London must be uncommonly healthy for I am made no offer.' He tried the same deal with Bellevue Zoo, Manchester also unproductively. However he did get a very dusty leopard from Macclesfield Museum when it was sold up and wrote Brown for advice on cleaning it.

His purchases were birds in cases or as skins, animals of all sizes even up to a young elephant, butterflies and moths in collections and shells in quantity. In a dispute over access rights for Macfarlane Terrace in 1863 he wrote to Mr France, Lord Abercromby's factor for the adjacent Airthrey Estate feus, that he could not 'sell any part of my property on account of my museum which has cost me more than £4000.' This would include building, buying the stock and library as well as the education of young John Murray. He was sent to France to assess the Jardin des Plantes in Paris for comparison with his grandfather's aspirations and had French lessons from a private tutor lodged at the house.

The scope of the collection was in fact world wide. By the start of the No. 2 Letter Book, November 1860, he must have had a large basic European stock since he specified the animals and birds of non-European origin that he required. He exhibited the first llama ever seen in Scotland and would have been astonished that 140 years later live ones graze the paddocks of Drumdruills. He already had enough kinds of monkeys and sufficient lions but wanted a different lioness in a recumbent position so that his cubs could be seen to climb over it in a group. When his relative Sir James Edward Alexander of Westerton was sent to New Zealand with his regiment in 1861 during Maori disturbances he took the opportunity to try to obtain a frigate bird and various kiwis via him or the secretary to Governor Gray. Lady Alexander was enlisted to prime officers going on shooting expeditions up country to look out for native fauna.

Sometimes his purchases were much closer to home from fellow collectors in Glasgow, from Small & Sons in Edinburgh or Buffon & Wilson in London both of whom were taxidermists and skin dealers. A single dealing was with Gordon Cumming, known as The Lion Killer, to help pay off the debt on his museum in Fort Augustus when he sold off some items. Young Murray was sent up on an educational trip to see the Caledonian Canal but also to spy out the opposition which was aimed at the tourist trade in that area.

The concentration is on quadrupeds and birds from Australasia and Africa with some American as well. Cases of butterflies or insects are bought as lots and not specified apart from some locusts. He considered buying fossils but then demurred when his funds were stretched. However he cannot resist a stuffed hammer head shark and some echinoderms that were offered. When it came to shells he relied on Captain Brown, a conchology specialist since his early Edinburgh days and who came up to Bridge of Allan to identify and arrange that part of the displays during special visits for four or five years consecutively.

Macfarlane was anxious to get Australian rarities such as black swans, the Tasmanian thylacine, kangaroos of various types and a Murray River crocodile so he could compare it with his Egyptian one, his Indian gavial and alligator from America. From India he acquired the skins of male and female thar and was chasing several dealers and menagerie owners for a really large Bengal tiger. Eventually he got one and convinced himself it was one of the largest ever seen in the country. Size mattered and he was not content until he replaced his armadillo and flying foxes with better specimens. Both hippo and camel, stuffed by Brown, were young beasts as was his elephant when it died in Manchester. He was very anxious for Brown to send it, repeatedly asking when it would arrive and then suddenly having to ask if it would go through a 3 foot 6 inch wide door.

For some of the quadrupeds he had to be content with a head with horns, the oryx and buffalo. His giraffe, designated by the old name of camel leopard, was to stand 13 feet when stuffed and one wonders how it then travelled from Manchester. He had three kinds of anteater, including the echidna from Australia, his Canadian lynx that cost him £6 was in a case complete with prey, the polar bear was small but the black bear more satisfying and he finally got two different hyenas. The greyhound he wanted put on a plinth which may have been of more local origin. Sculptured greyhounds are at the lodges of Keir House and a stone one is still on a wall of what was the back carriage drive of Manchester House, a villa he built about this time.

When it came to birds he had very large collections along with the symbolic stone eagles on his gateposts. Many of these were bought as cased lots but others were skins which he had stuffed loose with instructions that the wires came out of the feet for Murray to mount in displays by family groups or country of origin. Once he got his black necked swans he had seven different species and like all Victorians who collected he know his eagles, owls and particularly pheasants well enough to challenge a dealer who sent him the wrong type. The birds of paradise were sent back or the price discounted if they lacked all the correct feathers of displaying mode. Some birds he bought in lots he then sold off once he got another better one or which was just duplicate. The larger birds had to include secretary bird and full size ostrich while multiple humming birds, canaries and finches filled smaller cases. Wistfully he asked Brown if there was a dodo held in Manchester and it is unfortunate none of Browns replies survive.

Although nearly 80 years of age he continued collecting until he had to add two 60 foot long rooms to the original building with additional rooms above for smaller displays, cases of shells and the reading room hung with nearly 300 pictures of which he says only a dozen were fine. This he described as an Intellectual Lounge for the visitors who could take out tickets at weekly, monthly or quarterly rates with a family annual ticket costing a guinea. His own villas were rented by the half year and over winter lets. This was a place to go for entertainment or self improvement and when he had a free open day in 1863 to celebrate the wedding of the Prince of Wales some 972 visited the premises. Astutely he also had waxworks of the royal family at the time then sold them off for £100 afterwards. Entry was otherwise a shilling for casual callers or three pence for children since it was educational.

Although called Coney Hill Institute originally and collected on scientific lines there was no provision for further study at higher level. It never aspired to be a mechanics institute and he had given up on his earlier idea of a school of design. The letter book finishes a few months after Macfarlane read in his Saturday copy of the Manchester Guardian that Brown had died. He wrote to Brown's widow on 13 October 1862: "It was entirely on your husband's good offices that enabled me to make my fine collection of Natural History – In fact, I may state that he was its Founder and whatever merit ... it is entirely his and to whom alone it belongs." Certainly Brown's enthusiasm and special knowledge carried all along to the extent that he was lax about his accounts. Some years before Macfarlane had given to Brown a silver tea service in appreciation and now had to settle up with Brown's lawyer a bill for £182.9.2, hitherto neglected.

Macfarlane, always a difficult and trenchant man in business matters, now suffered bouts of ill health himself which did not improve his temper. He disputed his feu line and drainage through his property with the Airthrey factor, then with Lord Abercromby himself who was now feuing his land for villas and changing road alignments. He does not seem to manage to get his Lordship to come to see the museum and pointedly wrote to him: 'I consider this undertaking of mine will be a great boon to the families residing in the Eastern parts of the locality – so far distant as they are from the village of The Bridge of Allan, as it will be to your Lordship and visitors when at the castle ...'. He told Mr France it was 'the most extensive museum of Natural History in all Scotland or even in England out of London.' Indeed the guide book 'A week at Bridge of Allan' by Rev. Charles Rogers in its 10th edition of 1865 describes 'a place of remarkable attraction. The Museum includes a succession of apartments in two storeys of the building, and considerable additions are in progress of construction. The catalogue includes 20,000 specimens in conchology, upwards of 500 in ornithology and about 300 quadrupeds. The walls are decorated with interesting paintings, very amusing musical tableaux and a great variety of decorations. There is an optical saloon, fitted with valuable philosophical apparatus, and many eminently interesting objects. Finely executed casts from the antique have been added to the museum.'

This is the fullest description we have of the contents during Macfarlane's lifetime and almost the last. Macfarlane died in August 1868 aged 83 but by that time his grandson, after six months study at Edinburgh University and a major dispute with his irascible grandfather, had left. With a few courses of anatomy Murray first went as medical officer on a whaling trip to Greenland and returned on the very day his grandfather died. In that same year the Perthshire Natural History Museum was founded in Perth, birthplace of Captain Brown, but neither he nor his fellow enthusiast lived to see it.

Miller's *Handbook of Central Scotland*, 3rd edition of 1872, commented on the collections in much higher figures: ornithology 6000 specimens, mammalian 700, and add 20,000 specimens of minerals. The Erskine's *Guide to Bridge of Allan & Neighbourhood* of 1901 is the only one to comment that natural history items were in the new hall built by Macfarlane's Trustees in 1886. It had been intended that it be called the Macfarlane Institute but because part of the collections were displayed there it was always referred to as The Museum Hall. The museum function diminished as the main part, with casts of a section of the Elgin marbles along the balcony, was mainly used for public events and for concerts. The old hall of 1860 remained behind it, at the top of Coneyhill Road, until it was demolished in 1905 and Macfarlane Terrace closed off.

During the First World War the Museum Hall of 1886 was requisitioned and occupied by troops (as it was again during World War II). Some animals remained on view but a local story told that Macfarlane's prize Bengal tiger was used by them for bayonet practice! While the Museum Hall was run by Macfarlane's Trustees it faced bankruptcy in 1929. It was restored in 1930 and bought for the burgh council but the decaying beasts were removed. Most went to the burgh coup where a future archaeologist may ponder on the exotic fauna of this region even before global warming. Pictures and local history, with some birds in cases and the plaster casts ended up in the Smith Museum and Art Gallery, Stirling. Much was too decayed to retain or hazardous because of arsenic used in taxidermy so with their woodwormed cases there was another throwing away by 1970. Sir John died in 1914, famous for his oceanographic expedition on The Challenger and his editing of the reports. It is possible that, as the senior trustee, he gave some of his duplicate findings from that to his grandfather's museum which had started him on a remarkable career. His geological collections there suffered a much more ignominious fate as bottoming for the new road in the burgh about 1930.

All that remains are the eagle gateposts to my house, some pictures, casts and local history objects in The Smith and a marble bust of John Macfarlane. It was discovered in the café of the Albert Hall just a few years ago where he was decorated with a woolly hat and scarf having been dumped by Stirling Council, the successor to the one he tried to enlighten from his own pocket in the first half of the nineteenth century …. Sic transit Gloria etc. .

The only known photograph of the Macfarlane Natural History Museum on Macfarlane Terrace. The 1886 Museum Hall built by Macfarlane's Trustees is below on Henderson Street (formerly Macfarlane Street) facing a field now the Memorial Park.

BOOK REVIEW

St Saviours at 150. Published by the Vestry, 2006. £5. J. Malcolm Allan assisted by W.F.T. Anderson.

Most congregational histories are worthy, but exceedingly dull, strong on the architecture and the monuments, full of achievement and sanctity, mute on dispute and personality. But this, which covers the history of this Episcopal congregation in Bridge of Allan from its foundation in the 1850s to the present day, is a refreshing contrast, written in a very accessible, informative and impish style. What helps to flesh out the church's own records is the survival of personal correspondence to and from leading figures ['my Lord Bishop'– what an age is summed up in that title], shedding light on the realities of clerical life so often hushed up – the wife in the rectory having her breakdown while her broken down husband was under going treatment at Callander hydro. There were right from the start continuing problems of finance; as is wisely observed, a parish can survive with eccentric or slack clergy, but never without a good treasurer'!

Very welcome, and why this should be read by the wider community, is the ability of the author to set the church's history through the decades in its context, and in the early days that of a developing spa town at Bridge of Allan. It was visitors, either from Glasgow or England rather than locals, who provided the rationale for this new congregation – and tipped the scales to St Saviour's site: down below in the village rather than up at the Wells. Valuable light is shed on key figures in the early days of Bridge of Allan's development, Major Henderson and Lady Abercrombie, for example. As is made clear, the spa was to fade, and the coming of the university gave an impetus to change, as did also building in and around the area. Whether the congregation has taken full advantage of the new opportunities is a question which is raised, in the same spirit of honest appraisal that reveals the stresses on congregational life and in ministry in the later twentieth century.

Perhaps a little more concession might have been made to non Episcopalians, uninstructed as we are in the distinction between the Scotch order of worship and the Church of England's, which clearly did divide nineteenth century worshippers at Saviour's, or the force of ritual, but change is well charted through peace and war in hymnbooks, styles of worship and of ministry, and even times of services. Change is, of course, not always to everybody's liking – while it might be acceptable in 1916 to shift the evening service to 3pm for fear of a night Zeppelin raid, retiming 'mattins' in the early 1970s for perfectly good reasons caused great offence to some. But that is church life!

Available at Bridge of Allan Public Library and at the Smith, Stirling.

Alastair J Durie

BOOK REVIEW

Rome's First Frontier: the Flavian Occupation of Northern Scotland. D.J. Woolliscroft and B. Hoffman, 2006. Tempus. £19.99. 256pp. ISBN 0 7524 3044 0.

During the first century AD the Roman Empire continued its apparently inexorable expansion in spite of occasional setbacks, the most spectacular of which in AD 9 was the defeat in what is now Germany of three whole legions under Varus. Caesar's attempt to invade Britain in 55 BC was thwarted, but the emperor Claudius in AD 43 crossed the Channel and resumed the advance. In spite of the check of Boudicca's rebellion in 61, the occupation of what are now England and Wales followed, and Northern Britain seemed destined to be the next extension of the *Pax Romana*. Vespasian, the first of the Flavian dynasty of emperors, who had been commander of a legion in the invasion of Britain under Claudius, decided in about AD 77 to appoint Agricola as governor of the province with the presumed intention of completing its conquest. Agricola quickly subdued Wales, and then proceeded to North Britain, and by his third season reached the Tay.

Meantime the advance into Germany had stopped. It has long been believed that a defended frontier was built there soon after the defeat of Varus in the Teutoburger Wald, but it is now accepted that the *Limes* defences were not in fact constructed until the second century. The conquest of Scotland was supposed to be completed by the battle on Mons Graupius in 83 (or 84) AD, but the Highlands were never occupied by the Romans, although it is likely that there were some treaties or at least agreements with various tribes. Instead a frontier line of forts, fortlets, and signal towers was built, extending at least from a little south of Ardoch fort at Braco to Bertha near Perth. This line occupied the Gask Ridge north of Strathearn, and has been extensively studied, although new discoveries are still being made almost every year. It is now apparent that this was indeed the first frontier of the empire, earlier than the better known Hadrian's Wall (120s AD) or the Antonine Wall (mid 140s AD).

Much of the course of the Roman road along the ridge and many of the previously known sites are clearly visible on the ground, and can be visited. The most spectacular of these is the Ardoch fort at Braco, probably the best preserved Roman fort in Europe. The Roman road from Ardoch towards Bertha along the Gask ridge can be followed a good part of the way. Some of it lies under the modern road, and much more is still in use as farm tracks running arrow-straight and continuing the line of the modern road. Beside these tracks the sites of some of the signal towers have been cleared by Historic Scotland and are on display with information boards.

A great deal of information has been revealed in the 20th century by aerial photography. Woolliscroft and Hoffman are the Directors of the Roman Gask Project of the University of Liverpool. For a number of years they have been excavating new sites on and near the ridge, and re-examining by excavation or by modern geo-physical methods some of the older sites. They have carefully evaluated all previous work on the ridge no matter how eminent the excavator and have not hesitated to look again at the evidence and where necessary to draw fresh conclusions. Their book reviews the previous work on each site in detail, and brings our knowledge up to date. There are clear site plans, many reproduced from the original reports, and numerous other pictures, including aerial photographs. This book is an invaluable guide for any visit to any of the Roman sites north of the Forth. It does not cover the Antonine wall or any sites to the south, but there are other books for this.

There is, however, much more in this book than descriptions of archaeological work carried out so far in the area. Our understanding of the history of the conquest of North Britain by the Romans was that shortly after the victory of Mons Graupius the Romans withdrew and built Hadrian's Wall, and only made a limited return twenty years later to the Antonine Wall. It has always seemed that the Romans achieved an enormous amount in the short time they were north of the walls. The accepted chronology has usually been based almost entirely on the *Agricola* of Tacitus. According to this eulogy of Agricola by his son-in-law the conquest of what is now Scotland was entirely the work of this outstanding general. In their work on the Gask ridge Woolliscroft and Hoffmann, particularly in their re-excavation of some of the older sites using more modern techniques, have shown that the occupation must have been longer than was previously estimated. In the light of this new evidence there are a number of questions that have to be answered. They have come to the conclusion that we must re-evaluate the *Agricola*; it should not be regarded as incontrovertible historic truth, but more as the rhetorical tribute to a relative who was an outstanding public hero, a tribute in which by custom it was legitimate to make exaggerated claims.

Rome's First Frontier is a masterpiece which opens a new chapter in the studies of Roman North Britain. It is at least a turning point, perhaps epoch making. In the past we have been over reliant on Tacitus – we had to be, in the absence of other evidence. Now we have new evidence from modern methods of archaeology, ably and clearly presented in this book. It is to be followed by a detailed re-appraisal of the *Agricola* in a forthcoming book by Birgitta Hoffmann, which should be equally valuable and interesting. In the meantime *Rome's First Frontier* is indispensable for any one at all interested in the 20th century archaeological work on Rome's North West Frontier in what is now Scotland, whether as a guide to an individual site, or as part of the history of the spread of the Roman Empire.

Ron Page

COXET HILL AND THE NEW PARK OF STIRLING

John G. Harrison

Coxet Hill stands south west of St Ninians parish church and rises, according to the first edition Ordnance Survey map, to a height of 231.9 feet (70.7 m) [NT 789916]. It is now (2006) covered by modern housing and surrounded to the south, east and north by suburban Stirling whilst the motorway passes close to its western edge. Beyond the motorway the ground rises steadily to Gillies Hill, at 158 m the only other substantial hill south of Stirling and north of the Bannock Burn. This paper examines some aspects of the pre-urban history of Coxet Hill, in particular the significance of the belts of woodland that cross the hill.

There was a royal park to the west of Stirling Castle in the 12th century covering roughly the area of the modern King's Park. However, between 1263 and 1288, a New Park was established and enclosed, most obviously commemorated today by the Newpark Farm, close to Coxet Hill to the south. Miller argues that Coxet Hill was within the New Park (1). Whilst Duncan regards this as a 'doubtful assertion', both Duncan and Barrow include Coxet Hill within the park bounds on their plans of the terrain of the Battle of Bannockburn (2).

Only summaries survive of a charter issued around 1307 by Robert I (The Bruce) and the published version has been compounded from more than one original. The Newpark and Auldpark are involved, the New Park lands are described as 'prope Kirktoun' (ie beside the settlement at St Ninians Kirk) and, in one version, as being 'terris de Vet Pers Kokishote', which I take to mean, 'lands of old called Kokishote' (3). Kokishot beside Kirkton is recorded again in 1328 in one of the early charters of the Murrays of Polmaise and Touchadam (4). There are many later variants of the name such as 'Cokshot hill' (1617), Coxhoodhill (c. 1683) and Cocksydhill (1696); it is labelled as 'Cockshothill' on Roy's mid-eighteenth century map (5). The form Coxat Hill was noted in 1721 and Coxethill in 1726 (6) and it appears as Coxet Hill on Grassom's 1817 map (Figure 2) and as Coxet Hill with the associated farm as Coxethill on the six inch Ordnance Survey maps (1865 and 1923), though Cockshot forms continue to be used into the nineteenth century.

The Oxford English Dictionary defines 'cockshoot' as a broad glade in a wood where woodcock (*Scolopax rusticola*) 'shoot' or fly (usages from 1530) and 'cockshut' as (perhaps) the time when they fly, with citations from 1594. Rackham notes the netting of flushed woodcock in the re-entrant angle of Cockshot Woods and depicts a wood with two arms from a plan of 1613 (7).

There seems no doubt that the Kokishote of c. 1307 is the Coxet Hill of today. A detailed plan of the area was made in 1767 and, though it does not appear to survive, the relevant part was redrawn and printed by Miller (Figure 1). Coxet

Hill corresponds to Fields 5, 6, 7 and 8 on the plan, each field corresponding to roughly a quarter of the circular hill; the farm itself included fields 1-4 as well (8). On Grassom's map of Stirlingshire (1817) (Figure 1) the hill is labelled as Coxethill; two lines of trees meet close to the summit and one links to further trees on the north-western boundary of the hill. On the 1st and 2nd edition OS maps (Figure 3) it is divided by four narrow lines of woodland, corresponding to the divisions of 1767, with further small woods at the ends of the north west and south east radii. There is no sign of the wood on the modern 1:25000 OS map (2001) though a single strip of woodland is shown on the 1:10,000 Street Map, running between the two arms of Cultenhove Drive and continuing south west out of the built-up area towards the Motorway. Other strips also survive on the ground and are a very obvious feature of the hill as seen from the west and north and a significant amenity within the built-up area.

The absence of consistent representation of a wood on earlier maps need not mean that there was no wood or that it changed in form. The copy of the 1767 plan shows trees only in Enclosure 115, the substantial wood on Gillies Hill. Trees may otherwise have been omitted either from the original or from the copy as irrelevant to the purpose or inappropriate to the scale, as they are omitted from the modern 1:25,000 OS map. The variations on later maps are more likely to be due to the variable scale and cartographic considerations than to any necessary change in the reality on the ground. It is notoriously difficult to represent trees consistently on maps or to decide when a wide hedge becomes a narrow wood (9).

So, it seems very likely that there was some sort of wood, adapted to woodcock netting, in existence by 1307 and for some time before that, if it was, indeed, 'of old called Kokishote'(10). Planting, though not impossible, is unlikely at this early date and the form is more likely to have originated from selective felling of a larger wood, perhaps known to have been used by the birds. It would, in any case, be a serious undertaking and would strongly support Miller's contention that the hill was a part of the royal park; Miller argues strongly and persuasively that the Kokishot and the Park were virtually synonymous whilst Duncan does not explain his scepticism. Although there can be little doubt that deer would be the main quarry in the New Park, a charter of 1370 granted some rights in it to Alexander Porter and his payment included what appears to be a mirror or other lure for catching larks (11) so perhaps birds were a significant part of the quarry within the park.

Management, such as enclosure and selective coppicing, would be needed if the wood were to continue to attract woodcock. And management must have continued for it to survive, only likely if it always performed some useful function(s). It is even possible that it continued in use as a cockshot until fairly modern times when technical advances in gun design made netting of woodcock redundant (12). As depicted in 1767 and the first and second Edition OS, it probably functioned as a field boundary and might have been hedged or fenced. From the later 14th century the land belonged to the Murrays of Touchadam (later of Touchadam and Polmaise) and there may be further evidence in their extensive but still incompletely catalogued papers or in other archival sources. The site offers little hope of surviving pollen for palaeo-botanical study but there could be archaeological evidence to be found, particularly outside the main built-up area.

It has sometimes been claimed that the Scots reserve forces at the battle of Bannockburn appeared at a crucial stage on the top of a wooded hill at some distance from the battle and so terrified the English that they fled. Another tradition claims that they appeared on Coxet Hill, with similar effect. The possibility of a wood on Coxet Hill does not seem to have been allowed for – even though it must have been obvious to any observer on the ground. The evidence presented here is consistent with both these traditions but is not evidence that the forces were gathered on the hill or that their presence (if they existed) played a significant role in the battle. But the surviving woodland is a direct link with the period of Bannockburn, a designed landscape which Robert the Bruce would have known and used. It is particularly interesting that Bruce should have made the 1307 grant so shortly after his assertion of his kingship in 1306 and at a time when he can hardly have exercised effective control in the Stirling area. The woodland, which includes oak, ash, some Scots Pine and other species including invasive aliens, has a rather impoverished herb layer. It does not appear on the Inventory of Ancient Woodland for the locality. But, on the current evidence, this is the oldest identifiable cockshot wood in Britain. It deserves recognition, protection and further investigation.

ACKNOWLEDGEMENTS

Thanks to Stirling Council Archives for permission to reproduce Figures 2 and 3. My thanks to Chris Waddell of Stirling Council Countryside Service for checking the Inventory of Ancient Woodlands for me, to Stephen Digney for his interest, to Dr David Beaumont for suggestions and to Dr Fiona Watson for encouragement and helpful comments. Prof. Tim Birkhead and Natalino Fenech have my particular thanks for responding to enquiries about lark mirrors and related devices.

---

[1] Miller, E. 1922, The Site of the New Park in Relation to the Battle of Bannockburn, *Transactions of the Stirling Natural History and Archaeological Society*, 44 p.92-137.

[2] Duncan, A.A.M., 1997, *John Barbour; The Bruce, An Edition with Translation and Notes*, Edinburgh, p.441 and plan on p.447. Barrow, G.W.S., 1988, *Robert the Bruce and The Community of the Realm*, Edinburgh, p.213.

[3] Register of the Great Seal of Scotland (RMS), Edinburgh, 1984, Vol I App II 251 and notes.

[4] Miller, 1922, p.95 reprints this document; the original is now in Stirling Council Archives, Murray of Polmaise Charters, second series number 910.

[5] Roy, W., 1747-1755, Military Survey of Scotland.

[6] S.C.A. Murray of Polmaise, Baron Court Books PD 189.

[7] Rackham, O., 1986, *The History of the Countryside*, London, p.17 & Fig. 18.

[8] Miller, 1922, p.109.

[9] Rackham, 1986, p.205.

[10] Miller, 1922, p.104, citing this and other charters, sees the two as almost interchangeable.

[11] RMS I 317, charter for Alexander Porter, by David II, dated 1370. The Latin is *unum arcum cum uno circulo pro alaudis* and Innes suggests that this means a mirror for flushing larks 'as still used in Italy' (Innes C., 1872, *Lectures on Scotch Legal Antiquities*, Edinburgh, p.65). Mirrors were widely used for catching larks in early modern Europe, the process was known as 'daring' the larks, which were attracted by the rotating mirrors and caught in nets. However, the first clear reference to the use of mirrors is from 1583; Shakespeare, in Henry VIII, uses lark mirrors as a recognisable metaphor, suggesting that by the early sixteenth century they were familiar to his audience. The New Park payment was certainly some form of lark lure; if it was a mirror it is remarkably early but the case can neither be confirmed nor refuted on the present evidence. See Arentsen, H.F. & Fenech, N. 2004. *Lark Mirrors; Folk Art from the Past.* Malta: Privately published.

[12] Woodcockfauld, at NT 818855 is also within St Ninians parish and first noted (as Wodcokfold) in 1623, NAS GD17/399 but there is no cartographic or other evidence presently known of a cockshot at this site.

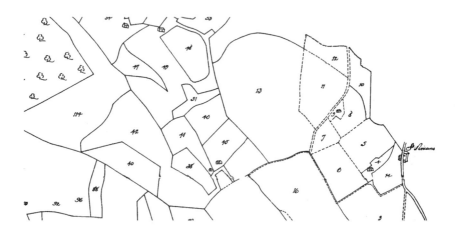

Figure 1. The area in 1767. Coxet Hill corresponds to Fields 5, 6, 7 and 8 and St Ninians village is to the east (from Miller, 1922 based on a now lost plan of the Touchadam area).

Figure 2. Grassom (1817) shows the wood for the first time.

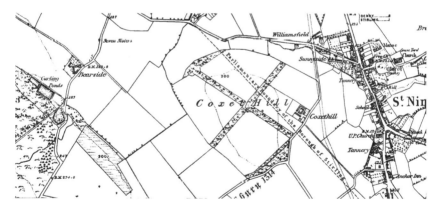

Figure 3. Coxet Hill and environs re-drawn from 2nd Edition OS of 1897. The 'cockshot' form of the woodland is clearly seen.

BELL OF ANTERMONY: BRINGING A TRAVELLER BACK HOME

David McVey

John Bell of Antermony was celebrated as a traveller and travel writer in his own time, and for many years afterwards. He worked for Britain in diplomatic service, as a merchant in the Ottoman Empire and as a physician at the court of Peter the Great, and also mixed in heady circles of plotting exiled Jacobites. And, finally, he lived as a respected Lowland laird on the southern slopes of the Campsies.

A number of sources can be consulted for a general outline of Bell's life, for example, Stevenson (1965) and McVey (2005). Here, we will review his story briefly, before bringing Bell back home to Scotland and highlighting some of his links with the Forth area.

John Bell was the son of a clergyman who was also the Laird of Antermony, near Kirkintilloch. Born in 1691, Bell studied medicine at Glasgow University and left Scotland in 1714 for Russia, and the St Petersburg of Peter the Great.

A Scotsman, Robert Erskine, Peter the Great's physician, welcomed Bell to the capital. Scottish doctors were no remarkable thing there: a contemporary English traveller, quoted in Cross (1997), wrote of Russian medicine that 'doctors are scarce and generally Scotch'. Bell, however, had the urge to travel and had no intention of simply staying in St Petersburg.

In 1715, Bell was appointed as physician on a Russian embassy to Ispahan in Persia. This gruelling mission, including the arduous journeys there and back to St Petersburg, lasted for three years but in 1719 Bell set off on another major embassy, this time to the Chinese capital of Peking. Soon after his return in 1722 he set off on a further journey, accompanying Peter the Great and his army on an expedition to the Caspian city of Derbent.

Bell's father died in 1722 and he is known to have been back in Scotland for much of the 1720s during which time, in 1725, Peter the Great died. Bell was back in Russia by 1734, this time working for the British minister in St Petersburg, Claudius Rondeau. He was on his travels again in 1737, to Constantinople. The journey concerned attempts to end Russia's war with Turkey, in which Britain was acting as a neutral broker. When Rondeau died in 1739, Bell effectively took over his post until his replacement, a Mr Finch, arrived. Bell then served as Finch's secretary until 1740. His next move was back to Constantinople where he set up as a merchant.

Bell married a Russian woman named Marie Peters while he was in Constantinople. The couple returned to Antermony in 1746 by which time Bell was 55 and had succeeded as Laird of Antermony. As he entertained visitors, and told stories of his journeys to Russia, China, Turkey and Persia, he was encouraged to write a book about his experiences. *Travels from St Petersburg in*

Russia to Diverse Parts of Asia (Bell, 1763) was duly published by R & A Foulis of Glasgow. The book was widely admired and respected and was quoted by figures such as Benjamin Franklin and Edward Gibbon who referred to Bell as 'that honest and intelligent traveller': even Samuel Johnson, not given to fulsome praise of Scottish writers, recommended the *Travels* to Boswell.

Bell described his travel-writing credo thus; '...it is the business of a traveller to describe places and things without prejudice or partiality and exhibit them fairly, as they really appear' (Bell, 1763). In his writing, Bell gives every appearance of remaining true to this aim, recording his observations coolly and simply. For example, he notes how '...the Chinese handle the two ivory or wooden pins which they use instead of forks with such dexterity...', perhaps the first recorded encounter between a Scotsman and chopsticks. He comments upon the goldfish he sees in China (still a novelty then to westerners) and describes Chinese traditional medicine that he has seen in use.

Bell the man discreetly intrudes into the page here and there. He reports without comment a Siberian hunter's tale of slaying a unicorn, and suggestions that woolly mammoths have been seen alive within living memory, but was clearly uncomfortable about hunting. When local people in Siberia organise a successful hunt in honour of the embassy to China, Bell damns the experience with faint praise: '...if killing harmless animals can be called diversion, this may properly be reckoned one of the finest' (Bell, 1763).

He praises Chinese costume as ideally suited to cold, wet climates; Bell was gifted a Chinese outfit when in Peking and was seen wearing it when riding out from Antermony in his later years (Cameron, 1892). No doubt it was handy for chilly Campsie winters as well.

The only other record Bell has left behind him is a 40-page handwritten document (now in the National Library of Scotland) known as *Sundry Anecdotes of Peter the First* (Bell, 1779). Here, Bell records his experiences and impressions of the great Czar, usually favourable: Bell was perhaps at his least objective on the subject of his benefactor, whom he greatly admired.

Bell lived until the age of 89, dying in 1780. His final journey was a short one, just a few miles west to the kirkyard at Clachan of Campsie where his remains lie still. Marie died in 1802 and is buried in the same place. John Bell's Scotland lies mostly to the south of the Campsies. Antermony House was demolished in 1926 and there is now a modern building on the site. Outside the wooded park (augmented in Bell's day with trees grown from seed he had collected on his travels) the estate has been broken up into smaller units and smallholdings, though Antermony Loch and the southern slopes of the Campsies remain much as Bell would have known them. Craigbarnet House, the home of Bell's mother, Annabella Stirling, stood a few miles west of Clachan of Campsie and has also been replaced by a modern structure. Bell's burial place at the Clachan has seen better days but is still identifiable.

However, Bell also has some fascinating links with the Forth area, and one of the best introductions to these is a curious article, entitled *The True Account of James Bell: a 17th Century Lord Provost of Glasgow and His Family* (Bain, 1895). This splendidly irascible piece corrects (with obvious relish) previous published versions of the genealogy of the eponymous Lord Provost, using contemporary sources; it also throws light on John Bell's ancestry and background.

(It's worth digressing here to mention that Bain's article appeared in a journal called *Scots Lore* which ran for only six issues in 1895. A pleasing blend of *The Scots Magazine*, *Notes and Queries* and *Forth Naturalist and Historian*, the extant issues are a fascinating read, right from the first issue and its advertisement for 'Drooko' umbrellas made by the Glasgow Umbrella Manufactory.)

We learn that Provost James Bell was the grandfather of John Bell's father, Patrick. Patrick Bell succeeded to the estate of Antermony in 1685 and served as minister of the parish church of Port of Menteith, until he was removed in 1689 for refusing to take the oath of allegiance to William and Mary. Patrick Bell's sympathies were Jacobite.

This Jacobite inheritance probably did John Bell no harm when making his way in St Petersburg in 1714. In Russia were many Jacobite exiles escaping the Hanoverian regime and trying to persuade Peter the Great to support future risings (Wills, 2002). Robert Erskine, Bell's sponsor, was known by British spies to be involved in Jacobite plotting, and was a cousin of the Earl of Mar, who led the 1715 Jacobite enterprise that fizzled out at Sheriffmuir.

The most puzzling thing about Bell is that he could be in such a hothouse of Jacobite plotting, have so many Jacobite links, yet by the 1730s be a trusted servant of the British government. Ironically, Bell's return to Antermony in 1746 coincided with the unravelling of the final Jacobite rising.

Publication of the *Travels* was funded through subscription: a number of people (named in the volume) undertook to purchase copies in advance. The subscribers include many Scottish nobles (the Duke of Montrose took six copies), Scottish merchants in St Petersburg, minor European princelings and a wide range of the great and the good. Many copies went to the Forth area – for example, to More of Leckie, George Drummond of Blair Drummond and the then Archibald Stirling of Keir.

None of Bell's letters survive, nor does the diary he kept on his journeys – perhaps if some of these came to light, we would understand more about the inner journey that took him from Jacobite circles to British Government service. If you have fallen heir to any of these subscriber copies of the *Travels*, have a look to see if any letters or other documents are preserved inside!

Bell was an intrepid traveller and a fine travel writer, and he deserves to be much better-known. In 1817, the *Quarterly Review* (quoted in Stevenson, 1965), described the *Travels* as 'the best model perhaps for travel-writing in the English language.' An even better epitaph might well be this, in Bell's own words from the *Travels*:

I had from my early youth a strong inclination to visit the eastern parts of the world; and providence afforded me an opportunity, far beyond my expectations, of gratifying my curiosity in the most ample manner.

References

Bain, J. (1895) The True Account of James Bell: a 17th Century Lord Provost of Glasgow and His Family, *Scots Lore,* 1 (3), 141-148.

Bell, J. (1763) *Travels from St Petersburg in Russia to Diverse Parts of Asia,* Glasgow: R & A Foulis.

Bell, J. (1779) *Sundry Anecdotes of Peter the First,* MS 109, National Library of Scotland.

Cameron, J. (1892) *The Parish of Campsie,* Kirkintilloch, D Macleod.

Cross, AG. (1997) *By The Banks of the Neva: Chapters from the Lives and Careers of the British in eighteenth-century Russia,* Cambridge: Cambridge University Press.

McVey, D. (2005) *That Honest and Intelligent Traveller, History Scotland,* 5 (3), 24-28.

Stevenson, J.L. [ed] (1965) *A Journey from St Petersburg to Pekin 1719-22 by John Bell,* Edinburgh, Edinburgh University Press.

Wills, R. (2002) *The Jacobites and Russia 1715-1750,* East Linton: Tuckwell Press.

AN EARLY HISTORIC FORT ON THE ABBEY CRAIG

Lorna Main

Archaeologists and historians have known for a long time that the low turf-covered crescentic bank around the summit of the Abbey Craig represented evidence of some kind of fortification. It is mapped as a 'castle in ruins' on Stobie's map of the Counties of Perth and Clackmannan published in 1783. The remains themselves, however, have attracted little visitor interest and there is nothing to inform them about the interesting early history of the site. Most of those who reach the summit of the crags do so to visit the National Wallace Monument and admire the spectacular views to be had in all directions. But the site's dominant position in the landscape had been recognised long before the builders of the Monument began their task in 1862.

The remains of the wall or rampart of the fort can be seen on the north, east and south sides of the summit. There are gaps on the north and south, through which modern visitors gain access to the Wallace Monument, one of which is probably the original entrance into the fort. The west side of the crag is very steep and did not require additional defenses although there may be a second rampart in the woods to the east of the summit. The area enclosed by the rampart is not large and would probably have included only a small number of buildings. Unfortunately, much of the interior of the fort and the rampart itself were severely damaged by the building of the Wallace Monument. The rampart has been additionally compromised in the past by the insensitive installation of services etc.

Pieces of vitrified rock have previously been found on the Abbey Craig, confirming that a fierce fire had raged within the rampart altering the nature of some of the stone. The high temperatures necessary for vitrifaction are generally thought to be the direct result of the burning of timber lacing within the rampart. It is not known if this burning was accidental or deliberate. Such 'vitrified forts' are generally considered to have been built mainly in the first millennium BC – i.e. in the Late Bronze Age or Iron Age, around 500-700 BC. In 2001 archaeological monitoring was undertaken on the installation of new floodlighting at the Wallace Monument. This identified two phases to the fortification on the summit and exposed a short section of the outer wall face of the rampart which encircled the top. As part of the project two charcoal samples were submitted for radiocarbon dating and the results of this were very surprising as well as exciting. The fort was dated between 500 and 780 AD, the Early Historic period also known as the Dark Ages.

These dates put Stirling firmly on the map at a time when Picts, Scots, Britons and Angles ruled their separate kingdoms in the four quarters of mainland Scotland. Stirling has long been considered to be a likely centre of power and influence at this time but most historians have suggested the site of Stirling Castle or even Dumyat as the preferred locations for the Dark Age citadel. These sites may well have been occupied at this time but the nature of the Abbey Craig fort more closely resembles other Scottish Dark Age capitals which are often on very steep craggy sites. Of these the best known are Dunadd in Argyll, Dundurn in Perthshire, Dumbarton Rock, and Burghead in Moray. Recent excavations on sites such as these have confirmed that the use of timber lacing was a Dark Age as well as a prehistoric constructional feature. In some cases the fortifications of the early Historic period re-used earlier forts but although this may be the case on the Abbey Craig, the limited sample studied suggests that both phases of the timber-laced fort belongs to the later period.

The Venerable Bede, writing in his *History of the English Church and People* which was completed in 731, refers to a city called Urbs Guidi, known in British tradition as Iudeu. It was one of the princely centres of the Gododdin tribe who also occupied the Castle Rock in Edinburgh. The dates from the Abbey Craig could confirm Stirling as the capital of the ancient British kingdom of Manaw Gododdin, which is still reflected today in the local survival of the place names Clackmannan, Slamannan and Dumyat. According to British sources, it was at Iudeu in 654 that the Northumbrian King Oswiu was forced to hand over to Penda, pagan king of Mercia, and his British allies all the riches of the city, an event known as the 'Distribution of Iudeu'. Even if the status of Stirling as the capital of the Gododdin is still the subject of debate, the results of the archaeological project certainly confirm that a Dark Age Citadel existed on the Abbey Craig.

View eastwards across fort rampart towards Dumyat.

CLACKMANNANSHIRE BREEDING BIRD ATLAS:
A PROGRESS REPORT

David Thorogood

Since 2002, as indicated in FNH Vol. 26 (*Clackmannanshire Breeding Bird Atlas* Andre E. Thiel), and subsequent notes alongside the *Forth Area Bird Report*, a Steering Group and volunteer surveyors have been carrying out administrative and fieldwork tasks intended to lead to the publication of an ornithological atlas for Clackmannanshire. Such atlases have been published for a number of areas of Scotland since the first national volume (following pioneering work in the English West Midlands) established the basic principles of grid-square mapping of breeding bird distributions for the British Isles (*The Atlas of Breeding Birds in Britain and Ireland* Sharrock, 1976). This local work will differ from this and from the NE Scotland, SE Scotland and Fife atlases in using a one kilometre National Grid square resolution rather than the more usual regional tetrad (2 x 2 km) or national '10K' (10 x 10 km) formats. This initially seemed ambitious, even given the 'Wee' County's limited extent, but now that the fourth year of the planned five for the main coverage of breeding status mapping has passed, success is in sight.

Buoyed by this progress the Steering Group, during 2005, reviewed earlier discussions and conclusions as to the possibility of achieving a year – round picture of the distribution of birds in the County. With a substantial pool of willing fieldworkers to call on, and no more than a simple presence – or – absence survey by species in mind, fieldwork commenced during the winter of 2005/06 on an anticipated two year programme to augment local knowledge of the avifauna. For this purpose the project *has* reverted to the tetrad format, making only 43 survey units to be covered during November-February, rather than the 198 complete and part kilometre squares involved in the spring/summer work.

The 2005 breeding season:

All Atlas projects recognise the importance of including survey data from a sequence of years, usually five, rather than a shorter period. Apart from the obvious difficulty of marshalling sufficient surveyors to cover an area in a single year, there is the desirability of allowing for the evening out of any annual variations in the number and spread of species due to (for instance) adverse weather or cyclical population fluctuations. The 2005 breeding season for example saw an (apparently) greater presence of Spotted Flycatchers and Cuckoos than in the earlier years, though still at a much lower level, for Cuckoo in particular, than might have been expected when the project began.

Twenty-two observers spent an aggregate of over 300 hours in the field during the year and as a result, coverage of completed or almost completed grid squares has reached 167, still ahead of the target figure for this stage. (In all, 42 volunteer observers have contributed records since 2002 and the total of recorded fieldwork hours to date exceeds 1300).

Compared to 2004 there was a slight drop in the total number of species recorded with 102 species being encountered. All but 14 of these were recorded in the possible, probable or confirmed breeding categories. In total 125 species have now found their way into the breeding season records. A few of these are unlikely actually to breed during the survey years. A singing male Brambling in late April in Dollar Glen technically made it onto the 'possibles' list but would seem to be going against the trend of 'global warming'. By contrast, Little Egret could eventually nest here at some time in the future (One or more birds have survived year – round at nearby Loch Leven and there are several records from the Falkirk side of the Forth).

Wren, with evidence of breeding in 126 of the kilometre squares, and Chaffinch, similarly recorded in 121 squares, are the most widely distributed breeding species to date. Blackbird, recorded from 115 squares, has now edged past Woodpigeon into third place. Carrion Crow, observed in 141 squares but with breeding evidence in only 109 remains the most widely recorded species of all. The species most widely recorded but for which there is as yet no confirmed instance of breeding (just a couple of probables) is Black-headed Gull.

Some examples of breeding distributions:

One of the initial drivers behind the Atlas project was Andre Thiel's interest in the occurrence of Bullfinches in Clackmannanshire and the paucity of published records available. It is one of several examples of species of local conservation concern (as identified through Clackmannanshire Council's Local Biodiversity Action Plan process) for which sufficient information has now been gathered to enable mapping to indicate their likely overall distribution across the County. With four season's worth of records now accumulated it is becoming clear that there are quite a few of these lovely birds in the area, but that either not many of them are nesting or, more likely, that their unobtrusive habits make it rather difficult to prove that they are. There is mainly, but not exclusively, a lowland pattern of occurrence but it is very patchy, except in the Tillicoultry-Dollar area. (Interestingly, the winter survey is already finding small parties of Bullfinches in this area, the largest being of 13 birds near the Tillicoultry golf driving range in February 2006).

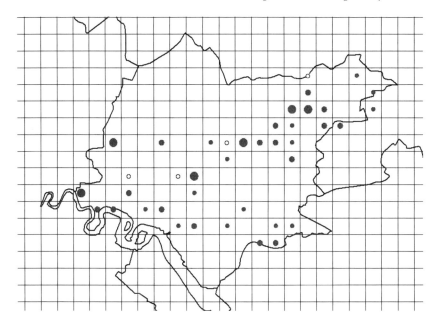

Recorded breeding distribution of Bullfinch (*Pyrrhula pyrrhula*) in Clackmannanshire during 2002-2005.

Key to Maps: small open circles = Observed only, with no evidence of breeding; three increasing sizes of solid dot = possible, probable and confirmed breeding during 2002-2005

Two other examples: The Lapwing is also mainly a lowland breeding bird in Clackmannanshire, and an easier one to find and to observe in breeding-related activity. There are more reports overall, and a much higher proportion of the records are of proven or probable breeding, but again it is perhaps possible to characterise the distribution as 'patchy' and to wonder what the reasons are for its apparent absence from some farmland areas.

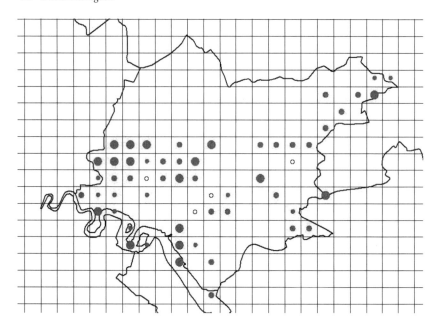

Recorded breeding distribution of Lapwing (*Vanellus vanellus*) in Clackmannanshire during 2002-2005. *Key as above*

The Skylark is a difficult species to miss and the song-flight gives a good indication that breeding is a least probable. The proportion of proven nesting locations is perhaps lower than might have been expected, but this is clearly still a widespread species locally despite severe declines documented elsewhere in the UK. It also illustrates well, (despite being only the thirteenth most widely encountered species) the excellent geographical coverage already achieved across the area, and especially the effort put in to ensure a record of the birds across the Ochil Hills.

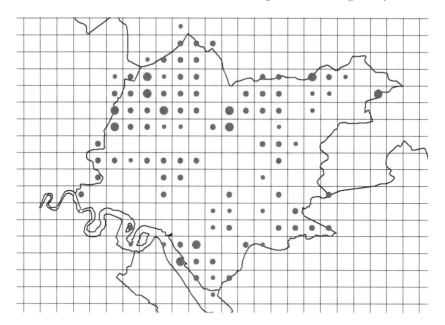

Recorded breeding distribution of Skylark (*Alauda arvensis*) in Clackmannanshire during 2002-2005. *Key as above*

The project to completion:

Only twenty-seven grid squares having significant land areas within the County remain to be surveyed for breeding species during 2006, the fifth and final survey year as originally envisaged, and complete basic coverage of the area is confidently expected. The Steering Group has been considering what further fieldwork may be needed to fill in some of the acknowledged gaps in the data collected so far.

There are two main concerns:-

Firstly, and inevitably, there is some variation in the numbers of species being recorded in adjoining areas of apparently similar habitat mix. Unsurprisingly, squares surveyed by professional ornithologists, experienced birdwatchers, and those dedicated 'amateurs' who are able to put in a lot of hours on their squares show the largest numbers of species commensurate with the habitats available and often also the highest ratios of proven breeding records to possible/probable occurrences. Judgements have to be made as to whether the lower totals in some other areas warrant further fieldwork.

Secondly, there are some species that are present but are just difficult to find. There are so far only 25 squares with Tawny Owl breeding season records and only 6 with Woodcock. Apart from these obviously tricky crepuscular and nocturnal species, and the 'skulkers' (Grasshopper Warblers, Water Rails and the like), there are several others that would be expected to occur – or occur more widely – but are not turning up on the recording forms. Goldcrest is a common and widespread bird but its very high – pitched calls are beyond some people's hearing range, and even when it is detected in its preferred coniferous woodland habitat, finding a nest is extremely difficult.

In order to improve coverage for such troublesome species, and to try to fill in any apparent gaps in coverage of commoner and 'easier' species, special surveys will be needed and these will be organised for the 2007 breeding season. The Steering Group would still be interested to hear from anyone able to help with these additional surveys and who is not already involved in the project.

For the Steering Group, advance work is already in hand to plan out the structure and authorship of the intended Atlas book. Authors are 'signed up' for most sections and species accounts and possible sources of artwork are being investigated. Clearly the end result will depend upon the finance available and a range of publishing alternatives are being kept in mind. The best estimate of a publication date at the moment is 2009. The project so far has been supported by the SOC, Clackmannanshire Council (via its Biodiversity function), SWT through Landfill Tax credits. Assistance in kind has come from BTO (use of mapping software) and others.

The composition of the Atlas Steering Group is currently:-

Neil Bielby	Chair, Treasurer and Joint publications editor
Andre Thiel	Joint publications editor
John Grainger	Minute Secretary
David Thorogood	Newsletter editor
Richard Daly	SOC representative and Art editor for publications
John Calladine	Mapping and Technical Advisor (BTO)
Don Matthews	Mapping and Statistics

CLACKMANNANSHIRE POND SURVEY

Craig Macadam

Clackmannanshire has approximately 60 hectares of standing open water. The majority of this habitat is found at Gartmorn Dam, while the remaining water bodies consist of rather small, scattered ponds (Thiel and Lindsay, 1999).

The Clackmannanshire Biodiversity Action Plan (Campbell, 2003) identified the need for a comprehensive survey of the ponds in Clackmannanshire to confirm the extent and wildlife value of this important habitat.

It is estimated that Clackmannanshire has approximately 15 hectares of ponds. The majority of these ponds are thought to be in the productive lowland areas, however some ponds can be found at altitudes of over 600 metres.

The ponds in Clackmannanshire have a variety of different origins. Some are natural sinks filled by seasonal rains that may dry out in summer while others are of artificial construction. They can be ornamental landscape features such as at Inglewood, Gean and Castleton; stock watering holes such as Craigton Pond or industrial water sources such as Delph Pond. Ponds are often naturally ephemeral or short-lived. All water bodies have a tendency to silt up over time. Emergent vegetation gives way to swamp which in turn silts up further to become wetland and then grassland and eventually scrub and woodland. Small water bodies go through this progression quicker than larger waters.

The pond habitat is not restricted to the open water area. There are also marginal, emergent and aquatic plant communities, and invertebrates that live amongst this vegetation. Marginal plants such as marsh marigold (*Caltha palustris*), valerian (*Valeriana officinalis*) and meadowsweet (*Filipendula ulmaria*) like damp or seasonally wet conditions. Emergent plants such as bulrush (*Typha latifolia*), spike-rush (*Eleocharis palustris*) and bur-reeds (*Sparganium* spp.) prefer to grow in shallow water. They can also include plants with roots in the pond bottom and leaves on the surface such as pondweeds (*Potamogeton* spp.) and water lilies (*Nymphaea alba*). Aquatic plants are usually completely submerged and can be either free floating or rooted to the bottom. This includes Canadian pondweed (*Elodea Canadensis*) and other waterweeds.

Some plants are only found under certain conditions. These plants can be used to investigate details of the pond condition, water levels, levels of pollution and chemical composition of the water. For example, finding an emergent plant on the dry land indicates that the water level is normally much higher and has recently dropped. Water lilies only grow in still water and not in rapidly moving water while some water crowfoots (*Ranunculus* spp.) actually prefer flowing water. Some plants, such as bogbean (*Menyanthes trifoliate*) are only found in acidic lochans. Similarly, many invertebrates react to changes in water quality or the quantity of water in the pond. For example, stoneflies, caddisflies and mayflies are generally intolerant of water pollution, however true-flies with aquatic larvae and aquatic worms are much more tolerant of polluted or stagnant conditions. In this way it is possible to speculate, with a fair degree of accuracy, on recent conditions within the pond.

Apart from three ponds surveyed as part of the Operation Brightwater project in 1991 (Lassiere, 1993), there is little detailed information on the extent and wildlife value of this important habitat. The purpose of this survey was to explore the condition and diversity of the macro-invertebrate and macrophyte fauna of a representative selection of ponds.

The project commenced in January 2004, with the majority of fieldwork taking place between the end of June and mid-August 2004. This paper provides details of the ponds sampled, together with notes on the species found.

Exercise Methodology

For the purpose of this survey, ponds were defined as a body of standing water, 1 metre square to 2 hectares in area, which holds water for at least four months of the year (Collinson, et. al., 1995) and included both man-made and natural waterbodies.

A desk exercise was undertaken in January 2004 to establish the number and location of ponds in Clackmannanshire and details of the relevant landowners. This desk exercise followed the techniques used to classify ponds in the British National Pond Survey (BNPS). The BNPS used data from 172 ponds in England, Scotland and Wales to categorise ponds depending on the surrounding land-use and underlying geology.

A total of 76 ponds were identified within Clackmannanshire by examining 1:10,000 scale maps of the area. Each of these ponds was fitted to a BNPS category producing the following breakdown (Figure 1).

Survey sites were selected to be representative of the coverage of pond categories in Clackmannanshire. Due to the limitations on resources, it was decided that only 20 ponds would be sampled. The 20 ponds were allocated to each of the pond categories. The resultant breakdown is shown in parentheses in Figure 1.

Sampling Methodology

The methods used during this survey were based upon the British National Pond Survey (Biggs, et al., 1998) and the PSYM Methodology (Pond Action, 2002) to ensure that the results of this survey can be compared with national datasets in the future.

Invertebrates

Samples of the aquatic invertebrates were collected using standard three-

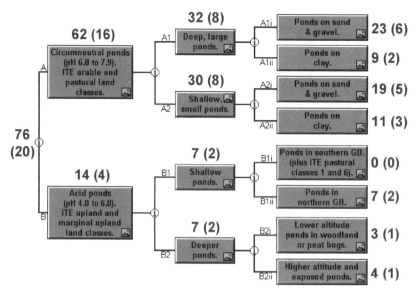

32 (8)
62 (16)
A1 Deep, large ponds.
A1i Ponds on sand & gravel. 23 (6)
A1ii Ponds on clay. 9 (2)

Circumneutral ponds (pH 6.8 to 7.9), ITE arable and pastural land classes.

30 (8)
A2 Shallow, small ponds.
A2i Ponds on sand & gravel. 19 (5)
A2ii Ponds on clay. 11 (3)

76 (20)

7 (2)
14 (4)
B1 Shallow ponds.
B1i Ponds in southern GB. (plus ITE pastural classes 1 and 6). 0 (0)
B1ii Ponds in northern GB. 7 (2)

Acid ponds (pH 4.0 to 6.0). ITE upland and marginal upland land classes.

7 (2)
B2 Deeper ponds.
B2i Lower altitude ponds in woodland or peat bogs. 3 (1)
B2ii Higher altitude and exposed ponds. 4 (1)

Pond Type Dendogram obtained from: http://www.ent3.orst.edu/PondFX/pondlife_main.htm

Figure 1 – Selection of ponds allocated to BNPS Categories.

minute hand-net sampling methods developed for the National Pond Survey (Biggs *et al.*, 1998). All the main mesohabitats in the pond were sampled so that as many invertebrate species were collected from the site as possible. Examples of typical mesohabitats are: stands of sedges (*Carex* spp.); gravel or muddy-bottomed shallows; areas overhung by willows (*Salix* spp.), including water-bound tree-roots; stands of Canadian waterweed, or other submerged aquatics; flooded marginal grasses; and inflow areas. As a rough guide, the average pond might contain 3 to 8 mesohabitats, depending on its size and complexity. The 3 minute sampling time was therefore divided equally between the number of mesohabitats recorded: e.g. for six mesohabitats, each was sampled for 30 seconds. Where a mesohabitat was extensive or covered several widely-separated areas of the pond, the sampling time allotted was further divided in order to represent it adequately (e.g. into 6 x 5 second sub-samples). Each mesohabitat was netted vigorously to collect macroinvertebrates. Stony or sandy substrata were lightly 'kick-sampled' to disturb and capture macroinvertebrate inhabitants. Deep accumulations of soft sediment were avoided, since these areas typically support few species and collecting large amounts of mud makes later sorting extremely difficult. Similarly, large accumulations of plant material, root masses, and the like were not taken away in the sample.

A further minute was spent searching for animals that may otherwise be missed in the 3-minute sample. Areas which were searched included the water surface (for whirligig beetles, pond skaters, etc.) and under stones and logs (for limpets, snails, leeches, flatworms etc.). Additional species found were added to the main 3-minute sample. The resulting sample of invertebrates, detritus and coarse sediment were fixed with alcohol and transported to the laboratory for analysis.

Invertebrate sorting and identification methods followed standard laboratory techniques. Samples were washed under a cold spray in a 250-micron sieve to remove fine particles and the Isopropyl alcohol before they were placed in the analysis tray. Samples were then sorted to select organisms for identification. Representatives of the invertebrates present were placed in Petri dishes or spotting tiles for identification. Identification to family, species or group was undertaken by close examination under stereo or high power microscopes with reference to taxonomic books and keys. The following precisions were used as a guide, however in some cases it was impossible to identify damaged or immature specimens.

Table 1 – Taxonomic identification precisions (after Biggs *et al.*, 1998).

Common Name	Scientific Name	Precision
Mussels	Bivalvia[1]	Species
Beetles (adults)	Coleoptera	Species
Beetles (larvae)	Coleoptera	Family
Crustaceans	Crustacea (Malacostraca)	Species
True-flies	Diptera	Family
Mayflies	Ephemeroptera	Species
Snails	Gastropoda	Species
True-bugs	Hemiptera	Species
Leeches	Hirudinea	Species
Moths	Lepidoptera	Species
Alderflies (incl. spongeflies)	Megaloptera	Species
Dragonflies and Damselflies	Odonata	Species
Worms	Oligochaeta	Order
Stoneflies	Plecoptera	Species
Caddisflies	Trichoptera	Species
Flatworms	Tricladida	Species

[1]Including *Sphaerium* spp. but excluding *Pisidium* spp.

Once the invertebrates had been identified and recorded, estimates of their abundance were made either directly from the whole tray or in the case of groups that were very numerous, by counting a subsample and multiplying by whichever proportion of the tray was counted. The estimated abundance was noted on the sample worksheet using the ACFOR scale as follows:

A	Abundant	>101 individual
C	Common	51 - 100 individuals
F	Frequent	16 - 50 individuals
O	Occasional	6 - 15 individuals
R	Rare	1 - 5 individuals

On completion, the identified specimens were placed in a glass vial containing 99 % isopropyl alcohol.

Macrophytes

The aim of macrophyte recording was to make a complete list of wetland plants present within the outer edge of the pond. Terrestrial plants and wetland plants growing outside the outer edge of the pond were not recorded. Wetland plants that were recorded include submerged macrophytes, floating-leaved species and emergent macrophytes.

Pond macrophytes were surveyed by walking or wading the entire perimeter of the dry and shallow water areas of the waterbody. Deeper water areas were sampled using a pond net or by grapnel thrown from shallow water.

Most wetland plants are readily identifiable using a hand lens. However, with a few species (especially fine-leaved *Potamogeton* and *Callitriche* spp.) it was necessary to remove a small amount of plant material for later microscopic examination and confirmation.

Results

Alva Ponds

Grid Reference: NS880962   **Dates surveyed:** 05/07/04 18/07/04

Alva ponds are situated on the banks of the River Devon just south of the town of Alva and are adjacent to arable fields. The ponds are dominated by tall swamp grasses with very little open water visible.

The smaller east pond is a swamp habitat dominated by reed canary-grass (*Phalaris arundinacea*) with some bulrush present in the centre of the pond. There is no visible open water. At the drier pond edges were neutral grassland species such as cock's-foot (*Dactylis glomerata*), tufted hair-grass (*Deschampsia cespitosa*), and meadow fescue (*Festuca pratensis*). Very few other plant species were present.

The larger west pond has a small amount of open water in the centre but is once again dominated by reed canary-grass in the shallower water and by bulrush in the deeper water toward the centre. Very little other vegetation was visible other than marsh bedstraw (*Galium palustre*).

Alva ponds are more a swamp habitat than open water. The larger pond still has some deep open water but this is likely to disappear in dry years or in the future due to silting up. The ponds play an important role in conserving winter floodwater from the River Devon and making it available during the rest of the year. Other species noted for the site include frogs and at least two singing Sedge Warblers. The ponds are ideal breeding habitat for these birds.

The invertebrate fauna is fairly typical of a lowland pond, however the presence of the freshwater shrimp – *Crangonyx pseudogracilis* is indicative of regular inundation of these ponds by the nearby River Devon.

Black Devon Wetlands (Existing pond)

Grid Reference: NS890916   **Dates surveyed:** 05/07/04 11/07/04

The water table around this pond is very high making exact mapping of the pond edges difficult. The plant species present indicate that it retains at least a high water table, if not permanent open water, even in dry weather. The edges of the pond are blurred by a thick growth of reed sweet-grass (*Glyceria maxima*) with marsh foxtail (*Alopecurus geniculatus*) and floating sweet-grass (*Glyceria fluitans*). Drier areas also include other grasses such as Yorkshire fog (*Holcus lanatus*), crested dogstail (*Cynosurus cristatus*), ryegrass (*Lolium perenne*) and tufted hair-grass.

The area around the pond is good quality wetland dominated by reed sweet-grass and wetland species such as celery-leaved buttercup (*Ranunculus sceleratus*), lesser spearwort (*Ranunculus flammula*), cuckoo-flower (*Cardamine pratensis*), soft and heath rushes (*Juncus effusus* and *J. squarrosus*). Celery-leaved buttercup is a locally important species and is well established on the water margins. Common spike-rush (*Eleocharis palustris*), water starwort (*Callitriche stagnalis*) and floating sweet-grass dominate the shallow water of the emergent zone of the pond. A very small amount of duckweed (*Lemna* sp.) is also present in among the spike-rushes. There is some marsh violet (*Viola palustris*), marsh willowherb (*Epilobium palustre*), great willowherb (*Epilobium hirsutum*) and marsh foxtail in the damper pond margins. The vegetation around the pond is best described as water meadow.

Waterfowl including mallard ducks (*Anas platyrhynchos*) and a pair of mute swans (*Cygnus olor*) with a single cygnet are also using the pond. House martins (*Delichon urbica*) are plentiful, feeding over the water and grasslands and drinking from the pond. Froglets and toadlets are common. Ringlet butterflies (*Aphantopus hyperantus*) are frequent to common as are blue-tailed damselflies (*Ischnura elegans*), small tortoiseshell butterflies (*Aglais urticae*) are occasional. The aquatic inverterbate fauna is fairly poor and dominated by water boatman species (Corixidae).

Black Devon Wetlands Large Pond

Grid Reference: NS895914   **Dates surveyed:** 11/07/04 25/07/04

This large pond is located adjacent to the River Black Devon and is the furthest downstream of the Black Devon Wetlands. Although it is the same age as the smaller pond upstream it shows little aquatic vegetation and no signs of salt marsh regeneration. The riparian vegetation in this pond is restricted to that found in rough neutral grassland and is dominated by tufted hair-grass. The pond appears to be very deep and slopes away sharply. This makes colonisation by plants difficult and contributes to the lack of aquatic and marginal vegetation, as these need shallow edges where light can penetrate through the water.

There are a few stands of reeds (*Phragmites australis*) in the shallower edges of the pond and hopefully these will spread as the pond matures. Otherwise the pond is largely devoid of vegetation at the time of this survey.

It is interesting to compare this pond with the small, shallower pond upstream, which is developing brackish characteristics. The larger volume of water appears to dilute any brackish water, as there are few signs of species such as sea club-rush (*Scirpus maritimus*). The main value of the pond is likely to be for wildfowl and the small islands may act as nesting sites, however the lack of vegetation to hide young birds and to feed species such as swans, moorhens (*Gallinula chloropus*) and coots (*Fulica atra*) may limit nesting potential.

Black Devon Wetland Small Pond

Grid Reference: NS895913   **Dates surveyed:** 11/07/04 25/07/04

The Black Devon Wetland Small Pond is located adjacent to the River Black Devon just south of the pipe/foot bridge leading to Clackmannan. The pond and area surrounding it show some influences of brackish water with species such as sea club-rush and lesser sea spurrey (*Spergularia marina*). Also present was the algae green gut-weed (*Enteromorpha intestinalis*), which is often found in brackish waters. Freshwater plants present at the pond margins include the grasses floating sweet-grass, marsh foxtail, greater tussock sedge (*Carex paniculata*), celery-leaved buttercup and pond water-crowfoot (*Ranunculus peltatus (R. aquatilis* agg.)). Terrestrial plants include Yorkshire fog and tufted forget-me-not (*Myosotis laxa*) as well as tufted hair-grass and soft rush.

The aquatic invertebrate fauna was dominated by Mysid shrimps, which are common in brackish water, and the larvae of non biting midges (Chironomidae).

Because the pond is shallow, unlike the larger pond downstream, the influence of freshwater inflow from the River Black Devon is lessened and the pond shows the development of saltmarsh vegetation sooner than other areas of the wetlands.

Brandyhill Wood Pond

Grid Reference: NS908954   **Dates surveyed:** 06/07/04 18/07/04 20/04/05

Brandyhill Wood is a medium sized wood located to the east of Coalsnaughton village. Power lines run west-east through the southern edge of the wood through a cleared ride. This ride has rough grassland and scrub. The woodland north of the ride is mainly semi-natural birch (*Betula* sp.) / oak (*Quercus* sp.) woodland around the pond together with areas of recent planting. The pond is in a poor condition and appears to act as a seasonal sump. There is very little water present and the wide muddy margins are mostly devoid of plants. Most of the vegetation reflects that of semi-natural woodland. Dominant tree species are silver birch (*Betula pendula*) / sessile oak (*Quercus petraea*) (or sessile hybrid) with ash (*Fraxinus excelsior*), with some beech (*Fagus sylvatica*) present. The shrub layer is hawthorn (*Crataegus monogyna*), willow (mainly eared (*Salix aurita*) and goat (*S. caprea*)) with saplings of the canopy species. Honeysuckle (*Lonicera* sp.) is present as ground cover and as a climber. The understory includes wood sorrel (*Oxalis acetosella*), Northern (*Rumex longifolius*), red veined dock (*R. sanguineus*) and clustered dock (*R. conglomeratus*), red campion (*Silene dioica*), creeping jenny (*Lysimachia nummularia*), figwort (*Scrophularia nodosa*) and buckler-ferns (*Dryopteris* spp.). The pond edges are vegetated by creeping buttercup, nettles and buckler-ferns. There is no emergent or aquatic plants in the pond. It is suggested that the pond must be seasonally higher as the muddy margins have very little growing upon them.

The best wetland on this site is a small patch of marshy grassland flush just south of the pond along the ditch and on the edge of the ride. This flush has an excellent variety of plants including lesser spearwort, ragged robin (*Lychnis flos-cuculi*), creeping buttercup, soft and heath rush, marsh bedstraw, marsh willowherb, water forget-me-not (*Myosotis scorpioides*) and spotted orchid (*Dactylorhiza* sp.). Ringlet butterflies are frequent in the rides and more open parts of the woods.

The invertebrate fauna is poor and dominated by small bivalve mussels (Sphaerium/Pisidium). Non-biting midge larvae (Chironomidae) are frequent, however the remaining species recorded, such as *Glyphotaelius pellucidus* (a caddisfly) and the Nemouridae (stoneflies) are more typical of woodland streams.

Brucefield Pond

Grid Reference: NS981997　　　**Dates surveyed:** 11/07/04 19/07/04

Brucefield Pond is large and rectangular in shape with an edging of mature trees on the eastern and western banks and small trees and shrubs on the northern and southern banks. There is a small island dominated by birch and surrounded by emergent vegetation. The banks are edged with soft rush, valerian, meadowsweet, marsh bedstraw, water forget-me-not and brambles (*Rubus fructicosus*). Emergent vegetation is dominated by a non-flowering sedge (possibly bladder sedge (*Carex vesicaria*), although identification is difficult with neither flowers nor nuts), which is largely concentrated around the island but is also sparse around most of the margins. Unbranched bur-reed (*Sparganium ramosum*) is occasional around the edges. Bog and small pondweeds (*Potamogeton polygonifolius* and *P. berchtoldii*) are also present. There is no sign of any waterfowl present.

Freshwater cockles (Sphaeridae) and the larvae of non-biting midges (Chironomidae) dominate the aquatic invertebrate fauna, together with the larvae of aquatic beetles and immature water boatmen (Corixidae).

In addition, newtlets were collected from the pond whilst sampling for aquatic invertebrates. Unfortunately these newtlets were too young to identify to species.

Castleton Pond

Grid Reference: NS981997   **Dates surveyed:** 19/07/04 20/08/04

Castleton pond is situated in ornamental policy woodland around what was Castleton House. Although the pond is artificial (there is a sluice network), the vegetation is very varied and natural in structure. There are large areas of emergent and marginal vegetation together with bordering wetland plants. The area shows little disturbance by people and has a wide variety of adjacent habitats including a small area of dry heath just north of the pond. Fungi, including a tawny grisette (*Amanita fulva*), were abundant. Around the pond itself, sycamore (*Acer pseudoplatanus*) and *Rhododendron* are dominant, and the ground flora is typical of semi-natural woodland, even though the surrounding woodland contains many mature exotic trees.

Marginal vegetation includes meadowsweet, water mint (*Mentha aquatica*), ragged robin and angelica (*Angelica sylvestris*). There are also many exotic species adjacent to the pond including *Rhododendron*, *Spiraea* and an emergent yellow Compositae species. Emergent and aquatic species include yellow iris (*Iris pseudacorus*), bulrush, annual star-wort (*Callitriche hermaphroditica*), common duckweed (*Lemna minor*), rigid hornwort (*Ceratophyllum demersum*), water forget-me-not, water-plantain (*Alisma plantago-aquatica*), yellow water-lily (*Nuphar lutea*), small pondweed (*Potamogeton berchtoldii*), broad-leaved pondweed (*P. natans*) and blunt-leaved pondweed (*P. obtusifolius*) – the only site it was found at during this survey.

There is a small area of dry dwarf scrub heath just north and uphill from the pond. Heather and wavy hair-grass is dominant with tormentil (*Potentilla erecta*), *Polytrichum* moss and harebells (*Campanula rotundifolia*) also present. At the top of this hill, against the perimeter wall, is a small stand of Scots Pine (*Pinus sylvestris*), with signs of raptor plucking amongst the trees. Ringlet and small copper (*Lycaena phlaeas*) butterflies are present, common blue damselflies (*Enallagma cyathigerum*) are frequent together with amphibians and a hunting heron (*Ardea cinerea*).

The aquatic invertebrate fauna is particularly good, with a wide range of species present. Of particular interest is the presence of many juvenile specimens of the ramshorn snail (*Planorbarius corneus*). This represents a new Vice County record for this species.

In addition, newtlets were collected from the pond whilst sampling for aquatic invertebrates. Unfortunately these newtlets were too young to identify to species.

Craigton Pond

Grid Reference: NS915893   **Dates surveyed:** 11/07/04 14/07/04

Craigton Farm Pond is a typical livestock watering pond. As a result, it has no aquatic or emergent vegetation around the pond edge. Vegetation near the pond edge consists mainly of nettles and creeping buttercups. At the time of this survey the pond edges were very muddy from low water levels and badly churned or poached by hooves. Reed canary-grass, meadowsweet and reeds are present in the adjacent roadside ditches, but have not colonised this pond. The pond appears to be partly constructed from an old building or lade as a wall makes up one side of the pond and there are numerous stones and bricks around the pond. Ash trees are growing along the top of the old wall. There is a moderate amount of windfall branches in the pond, which may have been placed there to prevent livestock from getting stuck in the muddy pond margins.

The aquatic invertebrate fauna was fairly poor and dominated by immature water boatmen (Corixidae).

In addition, newtlets were collected from the pond whilst sampling for aquatic invertebrates. Unfortunately these newtlets were too young to identify to species.

Delph Pond

Grid Reference: NS862949   **Dates surveyed:** 21/06/04 10/07/04

Delph Pond is an old industrial pond in central Tullibody. Some of the pond edges are artificial, however a small fringe of marginal vegetation has been retained. There is a limited amount of emergent vegetation in the form of amphibious bistort (*Polygonum amphibium*). The pond is surrounded by amenity grassland, footpaths and housing. A storm culvert discharges into a small settling pond, which in turn discharges in to the east of the main pond. The settling pond is vegetated with iris, reed canary-grass, reed sweet-grass and soft rush as well as great and rosebay willowherb (*Epilobium angustifolium*), docks (*Rumex* spp.) and other ruderal plants. The whole area is well used by local people for casual recreation. In addition, there is a sports court adjacent to the storm culvert area.

The main pond appears polluted but there are still many plants of interest. The pond is edged by iris, some bulrush, but mainly reed canary-grass and reed sweet-grass. Marginal vegetation includes water mint, watercress (*Nasturtium officinale*), brooklime (*Veronica beccabunga*), reed and floating sweet-grasses and cuckoo-flower. The vegetation suggests the pond once had better water quality than it has now. There are a few patches of amphibious bistort in deeper water.

The invertebrate fauna of Delph Pond is very poor. It is dominated by the water hog-louse (*Asellus aquaticus*), which feeds on dead leaves and other decaying matter.

Foad Wood

Grid Reference: NS965943   **Dates surveyed:** 28/06/04 19/07/04 15/07/05

There are two ponds in Foad Wood, which lies close to Meadowhill open cast coal site. The first, original pond is situated in an area of open woodland consisting of birch and ash, close to the main road. At the time of the visit it was largely dry with damp areas at the centre. The periphery of the pond is dominated by tufted hair-grass with *Polytrichum commune* moss dominating at ground level. Other vegetation includes marsh willowherb, soft and heath rushes. The central area of the pond is more seasonally wet as indicated by the dominance of reed sweet-grass with a ground layer of bog moss (*Sphagnum palustre*) and small amounts of stranded common duckweed in the dampest patches of bog moss. On the day of the visit the water table held about an inch of water overlaid by a deep layer of rotting vegetation, which appears to contribute to keeping the central area damp during dry periods. Larval and adult aquatic beetles dominate the aquatic invertebrate fauna.

The second pond, located near to the open cast boundary fence, was excavated a few years ago. At the time of the 2004 visit, the water level was very low, however during the 2005 visit the pond was at near full capacity. Most of the vegetation is on the very upper rim of the pond and reflects the surrounding grassland. It includes creeping buttercup, tufted hair-grass, toad (*Juncus bufonius* agg.) and heath rushes, common yellow sedge (*Carex viridula*) and bottle sedge (*Carex rostrata*). Emergent plants include several large clumps of floating sweet-grass, water forget-me-not, a very small patch of brooklime and frequent lesser spearwort. Contrasting with the 2004 visit when there was little water present, for this visit all the emergent plants were in shallow water. There were some algae but much less than seen at the previous visit. Vegetation in the drainage line just down from the pond includes selfheal (*Prunella vulgaris*), marsh foxtail, marsh willowherb, ragged robin and some lesser spearwort.

The area around the pond had a good display of common spotted orchids. Large numbers of froglets were seen and a newtlet was recovered in the invertebrate sample. The area around this new pond appears to be well used by deer, with many footprints around the edge of the pond. In addition there were also numerous froglets around the edge, suggesting that the pond is being used as a breeding site by frogs. Three small pearl-bordered fritillaries (*Boloria selene*) were seen in the grassland surrounding the pond as well as numerous ringlet butterflies. The damselfly/dragonfly fauna was particularly well represented with emerald damselflies (*Lestes sponsa*), common blue damselflies, blue tailed damselflies and common darter dragonflies (*Sympetrum striolatum*).

The aquatic invertebrate fauna of the new pond is particularly good with two species of mayfly, six species of beetle, two species of water boatman and two species of caddisfly.

Gean House

Grid Reference: NS873939   **Dates surveyed:** 21/06/04 10/07/04

This pond is set in a small, partly sun-lit glade within the wooded grounds of Gean House. It appears to be of fairly recent origin with a low wall on the near side of the pond. The rest of the pond has a muddy edge with duckweed on the damp mud, suggesting the water level is usually higher and has dropped rapidly. The pond is partly overhung by an oak and two beeches. The marginal vegetation is largely woodland in nature with remote sedge (*Carex remota*), wood avens (*Geum urbanum*), enchanter's nightshade (*Circaea lutetiana*) and creeping buttercup. The leaf litter is very thick and there are large accumulations of leaves on the bottom of the pond.

There is a large clump of Irises on the far shore, together with a small clump of marsh marigold and a single plant of monkey-flower (*Mimulus guttatus*) along with gardener's garters, a cultivated form of reed canary-grass. This, along with shrubs such as snowberry (*Symphoricarpos albus*) and *Rhododendron* suggest some artificial planting has taken place.

Inglewood

Grid Reference: NS878940   **Dates surveyed:** 21/06/04 10/07/04

Inglewood Pond is located in the grounds of an old estate. The surrounding area is a public park, which is well used for dog walking and casual recreation. The pond is medium sized with a heavily wooded island. It is surrounded on three sides by amenity grassland with the northern side shielded by shrubs. The parkland has a large number of mature exotic trees such as Douglas fir (*Pseudotsuga menziesii*) and copper beech. The water appears anoxic and released a foul odour when disturbed. This is probably due to a limited exchange of water in the pond and the presence of large numbers of mallard ducks, most of which show signs of domestic breeding. A large fish, probably a carp, was also spotted in the water. Grappling produced large quantities of rubbish and algae but no sign of aquatic or emergent plants. The invertebrate fauna is poor, and dominated by non-biting midges (Chironomidae) and water boatmen (Corixidae).

Mill Glen

Grid Reference: NS913977   **Dates surveyed:** 20/07/04

This small reservoir located in Tillicoultry Glen has been inundated with stones and boulders washed downstream.

Alva Glen Reservoir

Grid Reference: NS885982   **Dates surveyed:** 15/07/05

This small reservoir located in Alva Glen has been inundated by stones and boulders washed downstream.

Muckhart Mill

Grid Reference: NS995989   **Dates surveyed:** 19/07/04 23/07/04

Muckhart Mill pond is situated within semi-natural broadleaf woodland in a valley adjacent to the Hole Burn and just east of the Back Burn Wood SSSI boundary. Vegetation around the pond is more typical of semi-natural damp woodland than aquatic habitats. A few specimens of marsh marigold are present at the southern tip of the pond where there is about one to two feet of mud and leaf litter exposed by low water levels. There is also a sparse covering of common duckweed over the exposed ground and along the pond edges. No other aquatic vegetation is present. The Hole Burn runs north to south alongside the pond with a two-foot high bank separating burn and pond. The burn is clean and fast following over rocks and gravel with a series of small cascades just north of the pond.

The surrounding woodland is a good semi-natural wood dominated, at the valley bottom, by ash, pedunculate oak (*Quercus robur*), alder (*Alnus glutinosa*), wych elm (*Ulmus glabra*) and with some beech and lime (*Tilia* sp.) present. The shrub layer is of saplings and seedlings of these species with some red currant (*Ribes rubrum*) present. The herb layer flora is rich in diversity and includes wood sorrel, great wood-rush (*Luzula sylvatica*), woodruff (*Galium odoratum*), wood sage (*Teucrium scorodonia*), dog's mercury (*Mercurialis perennis*), herb Bennet (*Geum urbanum*), herb Robert (*Geranium robertianum*), wood horsetail (*Equisetum sylvaticum*), enchanter's nightshade, wood sedge (*Carex sylvatica*), male fern (*Dryopteris filix-mas*), oak fern (*Gymnocarpium dryopteris*), tufted hair-grass and wood meadow-grass (*Poa trivialis*). The area is rich in mosses, liverworts and lichens both on the ground and growing on trees. These include *Polytrichum*, *Thuidium* and *Dicranum* mosses.

Tree branches overhang the pond, which restricts the amount of light available to plants limiting the vegetation that grows here to woodland species. The only aquatic plant noted was a few sparse duckweed colonies. The limited penetration of sunlight contributes to the lack of submerged vegetation. The pond has a large number of windfall branches in it, which further shade the water.

While the pond is not rich in aquatic plant diversity, it is still a very attractive pond and an important resource for wildlife. It helps maintain the water levels within the woodland by catching seasonal floodwater from the Hole Burn and retaining it as standing water throughout the year. Woodland ponds such as this are potential breeding sites for amphibians, particularly newts that need ponds for breeding and live in damp woods during the rest of the year. The invertebrate fauna is fairly diverse and includes the caddisfly *Beraeodes minutus*, the mayfly *Cloeon dipterum* and the alderfly *Sialis lutaria*.

The valley woodland itself is notable in the diversity of plant species, dead wood, bryophytes and fungi as well as the frequent presence of wych elm and ash in the canopy. Unfortunately, a full woodland survey was outwith the scope of this project.

Naemoor

Grid Reference: NO013012   **Dates surveyed:** 11/07/04 14/07/04

Naemoor Pond is located near the village of Muckhart. First impressions suggest that this is a fairly new pond, however the landowners believe the pond to be more than 15 years old. At present the vegetation is consistent with the surrounding neutral grassland and is dominated by grasses including tufted hair-grass, false oat-grass (*Arrhenatherum elatius*), ryegrass, cock's foot (*Dactylis glomerata*) and Yorkshire fog. There is occasional soft rush, creeping buttercup and marsh thistle (*Cirsium palustre*) indicating that the grassland tends to be damp. The pond has no specific marginal or aquatic plants present, however, the water levels are good and appear to be stable and the nearby ditches have reed and floating sweet-grass that will eventually colonise the pond. The grassland in the surrounding fields and hedgerows show an excellent diversity of plant species typical of semi-natural neutral grassland. It is hoped that these species will also eventually colonise the pond margins. Aquatic invertebrate species present include the alderfly *Sialis lutaria* and the wandering pond snail *Radix peregra*. There were also numerous common blue and blue-tailed damselflies flying over the water, however no larvae were found so it is impossible to say whether this is a breeding site for either of these species.

Pike Ponds (Gartmorn)

Grid Reference: NS917945   **Dates surveyed:** 07/07/04 11/07/04

The Pike Ponds are adjacent to Gartmorn Dam, the largest body of open freshwater in Clackmannanshire. Trees and thick scrub surround both ponds, with the eastern pond being smaller and forming a largely reed sweet-grass dominated swamp with some open water around the deeper channels. The larger pond is more diverse in vegetation, with a dense swamp of reed sweet-grass on three sides with a sparse fringe of reed and floating sweet-grasses along the path side of the pond. It has large clumps of amphibious bistort emerging at various points in the pond. The very thick swamp in the south-west corner has a good diversity of wetland plants including lesser spearwort, hemlock water-dropwort (*Oenanthe crocata*), valerian, marsh bedstraw and meadowsweet. The water level in these ponds was very high at the time of these surveys, which made it dangerous to investigate the vegetation fully and to sample the aquatic invertebrates. Aquatic invertebrates collected included the water beetle *Hygrotus inaequalis*, the mayfly *Cloeon dipterum* and the leech *Helobdella stagnalis*. The invertebrate fauna was however dominated by the water hog-louse *Asellus aquaticus*.

Pool of Muckhart

There is no longer a pond at Pool of Muckhart. The area is now a small patch of marshy grassland mainly, soft rush, which may be seasonally wet. The local community has a plan to re-dig the pond and there is no botanical or entomological reason to oppose this.

In the Drumburn Farm Wood to the north-east of the site there is a fine example of wetland vegetation. The proximity of this vegetation would aid any natural colonisation of any new ponds. The wetland is part marshy grassland but has many aquatic species present. It is dominated by reed sweet-grass with duckweed, lesser spearwort, marsh foxtail, marsh bedstraw, sundews (*Drosera* spp.) and heath spotted orchids (*Dactylorhiza maculata*).

Sheardale

Grid Reference: NS952961   **Dates surveyed:** 28/06/04 18/07/04

Sheardale Pond is close to the B9140, however it is hidden behind a screen of trees and scrubs. The pond is entirely natural in appearance and has a near textbook structuring of marginal and emergent vegetation. It also has a very diverse botany and there were many terrestrial invertebrates including numerous hover-flies, and butterflies including ringlet, meadow brown (*Maniola jurtina*) and small pearl-bordered fritillaries. Large red damselflies (*Pyrrhosoma nymphula*), common blue damselflies and Northern darter dragonflies (*Sympetrum danae*) were also common around the pond. There were also abundant froglets and toadlets and, given the surrounding scrub and woodland, it is potentially a good site for newts.

Meadowsweet, soft rush and tufted hair-grass dominate the marshy grassland surrounding the pond. There is a broad strip of very wet marsh, in which meadowsweet and water horsetail (*Equisetum fluviatile*) co-dominate and soft rush is frequent. Other species present include ragged robin, heath rush (*Juncus squarrosus*), valerian, marsh bedstraw and some duckweed in wetter patches.

The shallow water at the pond edge is dominated by spike-rush (*Eleocharis palustris*) with unbranched bur-reed, marsh marigold, lesser spearwort, water forget-me-not, marsh cinquefoil (*Potentilla palustris*) and some water horsetail. Duckweed clings to the emergent vegetation and marsh cinquefoil form large clumps in deeper water and was in bloom at the time of the visit.

The marsh cinquefoil extends well into the open water but pondweed species are dominant here. Given the excellent vegetation structure, no grappling was done but small samples of the pondweeds were snagged using a wading stick, trying to minimise any disturbance to the vegetation. Pondweed species identified include broad-leaved, small and red pondweeds.

The aquatic invertebrate fauna was not particularly diverse, however it did include the Red Data Book snail, *Omphiscola glabra*. Other invertebrates recorded include the pond skater *Gerris lacustris*, the water beetle *Hydroporus incognitus* and the caddisfly *Triaenodes bicolor*.

Westhaugh

Grid Reference: NS884957   **Dates surveyed:** 05/07/04 10/07/04

This pond is almost entirely dried up, with only a small puddle of water present during this visit. The surrounding area consists of rough grassland dominated by soft rush and tufted hair-grass. The soft rush suggests it is seasonally damp but has not been a pond for several years.

The larvae and pupae of true-flies (Diptera) and the larvae and adults of water beetles (Coleoptera) dominate the aquatic invertebrate fauna. In addition, the ramshorn snail – *Anisus leucostoma* is frequently encountered, while pea mussels (*Pisidium* spp.) are occasional.

Woodland Park

Grid Reference: NS8999975   **Dates surveyed:** 18/06/04 10/07/04

Woodland Park is a popular local park, which is used for dog walking and casual recreation. The pond is of artificial construction (the pond liner is exposed around the input channel) and has a viewing platform and a sluice. There is a small amount of duckweed and a small reed sweet-grass swamp on the eastern edge of the pond and a larger one on the west. Marginal vegetation includes yellow iris, water-cress, brooklime, creeping buttercup, cuckoo-flower and soft rush. Also present are Canadian pondweed and monkey-flower, alien plants which can become invasive if not kept under control.

The aquatic invertebrate fauna contained running water species such as the stonefly *Leuctra moselyi*, suggesting that the stream is short-circuiting the pond, or that due to the small size of this pond it is behaving more like a wider section of stream channel.

It is reported that newtlets are regularly encountered when pond dipping at this pond. (Elaine Baxter pers. comm.).

Discussion

A total of 43 plant taxa (Table 4) and 68 aquatic invertebrate taxa (Table 5) were recorded during this study. Table 6 contains a record of observations of miscellaneous species encountered during the surveys.

To enable conclusions about the conservation value of these ponds to be made the macro-invertebrate and macrophyte fauna of the surveyed ponds was compared using a variety of metrics (Table 2) and converted to relative rankings of ponds (Table 3).

Biological Monitoring Working Party (BMWP) Score

The BMWP score was designed to give a broad indication of the biological conditions of rivers throughout the United Kingdom, however it can also be used to compare other waterbodies such as canals, ponds and lochs. The working party assessed the susceptibility of each family of aquatic invertebrate to pollution and assigned them a score between 1 and 10. Those taxa least tolerant, such as families of mayflies and stoneflies, were given the highest scores. Each family of invertebrate found in a sample is scored and the BMWP score is the sum of these individual scores.

Number of Invertebrate Taxa (NUMTAX)

This metric is the number of invertebrate taxa that have been scored using the BMWP system.

Average Score per Taxon (ASPT)

To take into account any seasonal or sampler variation in the BMWP score, the score can be divided by the number of scoring taxa present to produce the average score per taxon (ASPT). This score is independent of the sample size (a larger sample is likely to include more families, thus inflating the BMWP score).

Number of dragonfly and alderfly families (OMT)

This metric is the sum of the number of Odonata and Megaloptera families that occur at the site.

Number of beetle families (COL)

This metric is the sum of the number of Coleoptera families present at the site. The metric has a relationship with bank quality as well as water quality.

Number of mayfly, stonefly and caddisfly families (EPT)

This metric is the sum of the number of Ephemeroptera, Plecoptera and Trichoptera families present at the site.

Number of plant taxa (NPLTAX)

This metric is the number of pond plant species present at the site.

Average Trophic Ranking Score (TRS, NTRS and ATRS)

ATRS is a measure of the average trophic rank for the pond. This is calculated by assigning each plant species with a trophic score based on its affinity to waters of a particular nutrient status. The trophic scores used in the present study were based on work undertaken on lakes by Palmer (1989). Plant scores in this system vary between 2.5 (dystrophic i.e. very nutrient poor conditions) and 10 (eutrophic, i.e. nutrient rich conditions). Unfortunately, not all plants have trophic scores. This situation has arisen because the current trophic score values for standing waters (Palmer et al., 1992) are based on analysis of lake data only, and many plant species which are common in ponds occurred at too low a frequency in lakes to give them a score.

The ATRS value for a site is calculated as follows:

(i) The trophic scores from each plant species present at the site are summed together to produce the total trophic score (TRS).

(ii) The summed score is divided by the total number of plant species (NTRS) which have a trophic ranking score (NB not the total number of plants at the site) to give the ATRS.

Uncommon plant species index (PLCS, NPLCS and APSCPT)

The status of plants encountered during this survey was based on the findings in Smith, Stewart, Taylor and Thomas (1992). The status is based on the number of 5 x 5 km squares that the species was found in over the three Perthshire vice-counties (VC87 West Perthshire, VC88 Mid Perthshire and VC89 East Perthshire) as defined by the Botanical Society of the British Isles.

Number of 5 x 5 km squares	Abundance	Code	Score
1 to 3	Very Rare	VR	32
4 to 10	Rare	R	16
11 to 75	Occasional	O	8
76 to 200	Frequent	F	4
201 to 350	Common	C	2
Over 350	Very Common	VC	1

Each plant species is assigned a plant conservation score based upon their status (see above). The Uncommon Plant Species Index (PLCS) is simply the sum of the individual scores for each pond. This can be divided by the number of plant species (whether they are pond species or not) present at the site (NPLCS) to produce the average plant conservation score per taxa (APCSPT).

Scottish Wildlife Trust – Wildlife Sites Score (WS)

This metric is a qualitative score that can be used to compare different wildlife sites. For the purposes of this survey, this metric has been used to objectively rank the value of the ponds, rather than to decide whether the site should be a SWT Wildlife Site. The system scores each site depending on the degree of naturalness and the macrophyte species present. A score of 9 or above is regarded as of Wildlife Site standard. If the site scores below 9, a second set of criteria is used to decide if the site has other important features that should be considered.

Table 2 - Metric analysis of surveyed ponds

Pond	BMWP	NUMTAX	ASPT	OMT	COL	EPT	NPLTAX	TRS	NTRS	ATRS	PLCS	NPLCS	APCSPT	WS
Alva Ponds	45	12	3.75	0	2	1	14	15.8	2	7.9	58	14	4.14	10
BDW (Large)	19	4	4.75	0	0	0	6	17.3	2	8.65	33	6	5.50	6
BDW (Small)	16	4	4.00	0	0	0	13	42	5	8.40	87	13	6.69	13
BDW (Existing)	29	6	4.83	0	1	1	18	20	2	10.0	57	18	3.17	16
Brandyhill Wood	30	7	4.29	1	1	2	11	7.7	1	7.70	29	14	2.07	4
Brucefield	27	8	3.38	0	1	11	11	16.3	2	8.15	28	9	3.11	7
Castleton	66	15	4.40	1	2	14	15	59.1	7	8.44	103	15	6.87	16
Craigton	16	5	3.20	2	3	0	5	0	0	0	8	5	1.60	4
Delph	20	6	3.33	0	1	1	10	35.8	4	8.95	44	10	4.40	10
Foad Wood (Old)	16	4	4	0	2	0	4	12.5	2	6.25	22	6	3.67	4
Foad Wood (New)	85	17	5	3	3	4	0	24.3	3	8.1	31	14	2.21	4
Gean	25	8	3.13	0	2	0	4	15.5	2	7.75	22	4	5.50	8
Inglewood	17	5	3.40	1	0	0	0	0	0	0	0	0	0	4
Muckhart Mill	51	12	4.25	1	1	2	19	7	1	7.00	97	29	3.35	12
Naemoor	44	9	4.89	1	1	2	0	0	0	0	0	0	0	5
Pike Ponds	29	9	3.22	0	1	1	8	10	1	10.0	35	8	4.38	10
Sheardale	44	9	4.89	1	3	1	18	42.6	6	7.10	92	18	5.11	17
Westhaugh	27	7	3.86	0	3	0	0	0	0	0	0	0	0	0
Woodland Park	54	11	4.91	0	1	4	9	34.6	4	8.65	41	9	4.56	5

Table 3 - Relative rankings for individual ponds

Pond	BMWP	NTAX	ASPT	OMT	COL	EPT	NPLTAX	TRS	NTRS	ATRS	PLCS	NPLCS	APCSPT	WS	TOTAL	ATOTAL	RANK
Castleton	18	18	13	12	13	17	16	19	19	14	19	16	19	17	230	16.4	19
Sheardale	13	12	16	12	13	8	17	18	18	7	17	17	15	19	202	14.4	18
Foad Wood (New)	19	19	19	19	19	19	1	14	14	11	9	13	6	2	184	13.1	17
Muckhart Mill	16	16	11	12	4	14	19	5	5	6	18	19	9	15	169	12.1	15
Woodland Park	17	15	18	1	4	17	10	15	15	15	12	9	14	7	169	12.1	15
BDW (Existing)	10	6	15	1	4	8	17	13	8	18	14	17	8	17	156	11.1	14
Alva Ponds	15	16	7	1	13	8	15	10	8	10	15	13	11	12	154	11.0	13
BDW (Small)	1	1	9	1	1	1	14	17	17	13	16	12	18	16	137	9.8	11
Delph	6	6	4	1	4	8	11	16	15	17	13	11	13	12	137	9.8	11
Brandyhill Wood	12	8	12	12	4	14	12	6	5	8	8	13	5	2	121	8.6	10
Pike Ponds	10	12	3	1	4	8	9	7	5	18	11	8	12	12	120	8.6	9
Brucefield	8	10	5	1	4	8	12	11	8	12	7	9	7	10	112	8.0	8
BDW(Large)	5	1	14	1	1	1	8	12	8	15	10	6	16	9	107	7.6	7
Naemoor	13	12	16	12	13	14	1	1	1	1	1	1	1	7	94	6.7	6
Gean	7	10	1	1	4	1	5	9	8	9	5	4	16	11	91	6.5	5
Foad Wood (Old)	1	1	9	1	13	1	5	8	8	5	5	6	10	2	75	5.4	4
Craigton	1	4	2	18	4	1	7	1	1	1	4	5	4	2	55	3.9	3
Westhaugh	8	8	8	1	13	1	1	1	1	1	1	1	1	1	47	3.4	2
Inglewood	4	4	6	12	1	1	1	1	1	1	1	1	1	2	37	2.6	1

There are a wide variety of pond habitats present in Clackmannanshire. These ponds vary in age and construction from the newly dug pond at Woodland Park to the long-established natural pond at Sheardale.

The ponds at Castleton, Sheardale and Foad Wood (New) represent some of the best examples of ponds in Clackmannanshire, and possibly Central Scotland. They hold varied assemblages of both macrophytes and invertebrates, including *Omphiscola glabra*, a red data book snail, from the pond at Sheardale. The new pond at Foad Wood is an excellent example of pond creation. The pond was excavated less than five years ago and the invertebrate fauna has since developed to be one of the most diverse assemblages encountered during these surveys. By contrast, the vegetation structure in the pond at Sheardale has developed over many decades and is of exceptional quality. The pond at Castleton combines exceptional macroinvertebrate and macrophyte faunas to produce the best pond biodiversity in Clackmannan-shire.

Many of the ponds have little threat to their wellbeing, however some such as Foad Wood (New) and Brandyhill Wood are in danger of drying out completely during summer months. Others such as the ponds at Alva, Foad Wood (Old), Pike Ponds and the small pond at the Black Devon Wetlands require no active management. The ponds at Inglewood and the Delph Pond also require little management, instead they need to be allowed to develop naturally, by allowing marginal vegetation to remain long and therefore softening the hard, artificial edges of these man-made ponds.

In summary, Clackmannanshire's ponds are an important natural asset, which cover all stages in the natural succession of ponds. Whilst many of the ponds visited during this survey are in their prime, others are in the advance stages of succession with a few such as Westhaugh and Foad Wood (Old) being little more than wet grassland during the summer months. It is essential that these ponds be replaced with newly dug ponds to ensure that the unique fauna of Clackmannanshire's ponds continues to prosper.

Table 4 – Macrophyte species recorded and their distribution.

Scientific Name	Common Name	Woodland Park	Westhaugh	Sheardale	Pool of Muckart	Pike Ponds	Naemoor	Muckhart Mill	Inglewood	Gean	Foad (Old)	Foad (New)	Delph	Craigton	Castleton	Brucefield	Brandyhill	BDW (Small)	BDW (Large)	BDW (Existing)	Alva Ponds
Alisma plantago-aquatica	Water Plantain							*							*						
Alnus glutinosa	Alder											*						*		*	
Alopecurus geniculatus	Marsh Foxtail							*													
Arrhenatherum elatius	False Oat-grass																*				
Betula pendula	Silver Birch															*					
Betula sp.	Birch														*						
Callitriche hermaphroditica	Annual Star-wort																			*	
Callitriche stagnalis	Water Starwort	*		*				*		*			*								
Caltha palustris	Marsh Marigold									*								*		*	
Cardamine pratensis	Cuckoo-flower							*													
Carex paniculata	Greater Tussock Sedge											*									*
Carex remota	Remote Sedge															*					*
Carex rostrata	Bottle Sedge							*													*
Carex sp.	Sedge											*									
Carex sylvatica	Wood Sedge							*							*						
Carex viridula	Common Yellow Sedge																				
Ceratophyllum demersum	Rigid Hornwort													*					*		
Circaea lutetiana	Enchanter's Nightshade						*														
Cirsium arvense	Creeping Thistle																				
Cirsium palustre	Marsh Thistle																*			*	
Conopodium majus	Pignut																				
Crataegus monogyna	Hawthorn																*				
Cynosurus cristatus	Crested Dogstail																				
Dactylis glomerata	Cock's-foot																				
Dactylorhiza sp.	Spotted Orchid																				
Deschampsia cespitosa	Tufted Hair-grass		*				*	*			*	*						*	*	*	*

Table 4 – Macrophyte species recorded and their distribution (cont.).

Scientific Name	Common Name	Woodland Park	Westhaugh	Sheardale	Pool of Muckart	Pike Ponds	Naemoor	Muckhart Mill	Inglewood	Gean	Foad (Old)	Foad (New)	Delph	Craigton	Castleton	Brucefield	Brandyhill	BDW (Small)	BDW (Large)	BDW (Existing)	Alva Ponds
Dicranum sp.	A moss							*													
Dryopteris filix-mas	Male Fern							*													
Dryopteris sp.	Buckler-fern																*				
Eleocharis palustris	Spike-rush			*																*	
Elodea canadensis	Canadian Pondweed	*																			
Enteromorpha intestinalis	Green Gut-weed																	*			
Epilobium ciliatum	American Willowherb																				*
Epilobium hirsutum	Great Willowherb																			*	*
Epilobium palustre	Marsh Willowherb										*						*			*	
Equisetum fluviatile	Water Horsetail			*																	
Equisetum pratense	Shady Horsetail							*													
Fagus sylvatica	Beech							*													*
Festuca pratensis	Meadow Fescue			*											*						*
Filipendula ulmaria	Meadowsweet															*					
Fraxinus excelsior	Ash							*													
Galium odoratum	Woodruff			*				*													*
Galium palustre	Marsh Bedstraw															*	*				
Geranium robertianum	Herb Robert							*													
Geum urbanum	Herb Bennet							*													
Glyceria fluitans	Floating Swee-grass	*				*	*				*	*	*					*	*	*	
Glyceria maxima	Reed Sweet-grass												*							*	
Gymnocarpium dryopteris	Oak Fern						*	*						*							
Holcus lanatus	Yorkshire Fog	*				*							*		*			*		*	
Iris pseudacorus	Yellow Iris											*					▲				
Juncus bufonius agg.	Toad Rush					*															
Juncus effusus	Soft Rush	*	*	*			*				*		*			*		*		*	

Table 4 – Macrophyte species recorded and their distribution (cont.).

Site	Heath Rush	Common Duckweed	Ryegrass	Great Wood-rush	Ragged Robin	Water Mint	Dog's Mercury	Monkey-flower	Tufted Forget-me-not	Water Forget-me-not	Watercress	Yellow Water-lily	White Water-lily	Hemlock Water-dropwort	Wood Sorrel	Gardener's Garters	Reed Canary-grass	Common Reed	Wood Meadow-grass	Amphibious Bistort	Hair-moss	A moss	Red Pondweed	Small Pondweed	Broad-leaved Pondweed	Blunt-leaved Pondweed
Woodland Park	*							*				*														
Westhaugh	*																									
Sheardale	*	*		*						*														*	*	*
Pool of Muckart																										
Pike Ponds														*						*						
Naemoor																										
Muckhart Mill	*			*			*								*				*				*			
Inglewood																										
Gean	*							*								*										
Foad (Old)	*	*																			*					
Foad (New)	*				*						*															
Delph						*						*								*						
Craigton			*																							
Castleton	*				*	*					*		*	*										*	*	*
Brucefield											*												*			
Brandyhill	*				*				*																	
BDW (Small)									*									*								
BDW (Large)																		*								
BDW (Existing)	*		*																							
Alva Ponds			*														*									

Scientific Name / Common Name

Juncus squarrosus — Heath Rush
Lemna minor — Common Duckweed
Lolium perenne — Ryegrass
Luzula sylvatica — Great Wood-rush
Lychnis flos-cuculi — Ragged Robin
Mentha aquatica — Water Mint
Mercurialis perennis — Dog's Mercury
Mimulus guttatus — Monkey-flower
Myosotis laxa — Tufted Forget-me-not
Myosotis scorpioides — Water Forget-me-not
Nasturtium officinale — Watercress
Nuphar lutea — Yellow Water-lily
Nymphaea alba — White Water-lily
Oenanthe crocata — Hemlock Water-dropwort
Oxalis acetosella — Wood Sorrel
Phalaris arundinacea — Gardener's Garters
Phalaris arundinacea — Reed Canary-grass
Phragmites australis — Common Reed
Poa trivialis — Wood Meadow-grass
Polygonum amphibium — Amphibious Bistort
Polytrichum commune — Hair-moss
Polytrichum sp. — A moss
Potamogeton alpinus — Red Pondweed
Potamogeton berchtoldii — Small Pondweed
Potamogeton natans — Broad-leaved Pondweed
Potamogeton obtusifolius — Blunt-leaved Pondweed

Table 4 – Macrophyte species recorded and their distribution (cont.).

Scientific Name	Common Name	Woodland Park	Westhaugh	Sheardale	Pool of Muckart	Pike Ponds	Naemoor	Muckhart Mill	Inglewood	Gean	Foad (Old)	Foad (New)	Delph	Craigton	Castleton	Brucefield	Brandyhill	BDW (Small)	BDW (Large)	BDW (Existing)	Alva Ponds
Potamogeton polygonifolius	Bog Pondweed			*												*					
Potentilla palustris	Marsh Cinquefoil																*				
Quercus petraea	Sessile Oak							*													
Quercus robur	Pedunculate Oak			*		*						*					*			*	
Ranunculus flammula	Lesser Spearwort																	*			
Ranunculus peltatus (R. aquatilis agg.)	Pond Water-Crowfoot																				
Ranunculus repens	Creeping Buttercup						*					*					*			*	
Ranunculus sceleratus	Celery-leaved Buttercup																	*		*	
Ribes rubrum	Red Currant							*													
Rubus fruticosus	Bramble																				
Salix aurita	Eared Willow																*				
Salix caprea	Goat Willow																*				*
Scirpus maritimus	Sea Club-rush															*		*			
Sparganium emersum	Unbranched Bur-reed			*															*		
Spergularia marina	Lesser Sea Spurrey															*		*			
Sphagnum palustre	Bog moss										*										
Stachys palustris	Marsh Woundwort																				*
Stachys sylvatica	Hedge Woundwort							*	*												
Teucrium scorodonia	Wood Sage							*													
Thuidium sp.	A moss							*													
Tilia sp.	Lime							*													
Typha latifolia	Bulrush			*									*		*						*
Ulmus glabra	Wych Elm							*											*		
Urtica dioica	Nettle													*			*				
Valeriana officinalis	Valerian			*		*															
Veronica beccabunga	Brooklime	*										*	*			*					
Viola palustris	Marsh Violet																			*	

Table 5 – Macroinvertebrate species recorded and their distribution.

Scientific Name	Common Name	Woodland Park	Westhaugh	Sheardale	Pool of Muckart	Pike Ponds	Naemoor	Muckhart Mill	Inglewood	Gean	Foad (Old)	Foad (New)	Delph	Craigton	Castleton	Brucefield	Brandyhill	BDW (Small)	BDW (Large)	BDW (Existing)	Alva Ponds
Agabus arcticus	Diving Beetle										*										
Agabus bipustulatus	Diving Beetle		*							*	*										
Agabus nebulosus	Diving Beetle													*							
Anisus leucostoma	Ramshorn Snail		*							*											*
Asellus aquaticus	Water Hog-louse	*				*			*	*			*								*
Assorted Diptera larvae (incl. Tipulidae, Psychodidae and Ptychopteridae)	True-fly larvae																*				
Assorted Diptera pupae (incl. Tipulidae, Psychodidae and Ptychopteridae)	True-fly pupae		*														*				
Beraeodes minutus	Caddisfly																				
Berosus sp.	Water Beetle		*					*										*			
Caenis horaria	Mayfly										*										
Callicorixa praeusta	Water Boatman						*														*
Callicorixa wollastoni	Water Boatman																			*	*
Ceratopogonidae	Biting midge																			*	
Chaoboridae	Phantom midge											*					*				
Chironomidae	Non-biting midge					*				*		*			*						
Cladocera (various)	Water fleas	*		*		*	*	*	*	*		*	*	*	*	*	*	*	*	*	*
Cloeon dipterum	Mayfly	*												*	*	*				*	*
Cloeon simile	Mayfly					*		*					*		*						*
Cloeon sp.	Mayfly											*									
Coelambus confluens	Water Beetle											*			*						
Corixa punctata	Water Boatman																				
Corophium sp.	Freshwater Shrimp															*		*	*		
Crangonyx pseudogracilis	Freshwater Shrimp																				*
Crunoecia irrorata	Caddisfly	*																			

Table 5 – Macroinvertebrate species recorded and their distribution (cont).

Site	Culicidae (Mosquito)	Cymatia bonsdorffii (Water Boatman)	Cyrnus flavidus (Caddisfly)	Enallagma cyathigerum (Damselfly)	Erpobdella sp. (Freshwater Leech)	Gammarus zaddachi (Freshwater Shrimp)	Gerris lacustris (Pond Skater)	Glossiphonia complanata (Freshwater Leech)	Glossiphonia heteroclita (Freshwater Leech)	Glyphotaelius pellucidus (Caddisfly)	Gyraulus albus (Ramshorn Snail)	Haliplus confinis (Water Beetle)	Haliplus ruficollis group (Water Beetle)	Helobdella stagnalis (Freshwater Leech)	Helophorus brevipalpis (Water Beetle)	Helophorus sp. (Water Beetle)	Helophorus sp. poss. H. brevipalpis (Water Beetle)	Hesperocorixa sahlbergi (Water Boatman)	Holocentropus picicornis (Caddisfly)	Holocentropus stagnalis (Caddisfly)	Hydracarina (Aquatic Mite)	Hydracarina (poss. Piona sp.) (Aquatic Mite)	Hydroporus incognitus (Water Beetle)	Hydroporus nigrita (Water Beetle)	Hydroporus sp. 1 (Water Beetle)	Hydroporus sp. 2 (Water Beetle)
Woodland Park																										
Westhaugh				*									*													
Sheardale			*			*						*										*				
Pool of Muckart																										
Pike Ponds													*							*						
Naemoor																*										
Muckhart Mill								*		*			*							*						
Inglewood	*												*													
Gean												*													*	*
Foad (Old)														*											*	*
Foad (New)											*		*	*			*	*							*	*
Delph																										
Craigton													*										*			
Castleton		*	*				*					*	*						*	*						
Brucefield													*							*						
Brandyhill									*																	
BDW (Small)																										
BDW (Large)					*																					
BDW (Existing)						*																				
Alva Ponds	*													*								*				

Table 5 – Macroinvertebrate species recorded and their distribution (cont.).

Scientific Name	Common Name	Woodland Park	Westhaugh	Sheardale	Pool of Muckart	Pike Ponds	Naemoor	Muckhart Mill	Inglewood	Gean	Foad (Old)	Foad (New)	Delph	Craigton	Castleton	Brucefield	Brandyhill	BDW (Small)	BDW (Large)	BDW (Existing)	Alva Ponds
Hydroporus sp. poss. *H. nigrita*	Water Beetle		*																		*
Hygrotus inaequalis	Water Beetle																				
Imm. Corixidae	Water Boatman					*	*	*	*			*	*	*	*	*		*	*	*	
Imm. *Gammarus* sp. poss. *G. pulex*	Freshwater Shrimp	*					*														
Imm. *Gammarus* sp. prob. *G. lacustris*	Freshwater Shrimp							*							*						
Imm. Gerridae	Pond Skater							*		*											
Imm. *Notonecta* sp. (prob. *N. glauca*)	Backswimmer			*																	
Indet. Baetidae	Mayfly					*															
Indet. Dytiscidae adult	Water Beetle											*									
Indet. Dytiscidae larvae	Water Beetle															*					
Indet. Erpobdellidae	Freshwater Leech	*	*	*		*		*		*	*	*	*	*	*	*	*			*	*
Indet. Helodidae larvae	Water Beetle					*															
Indet. Hydrobiidae	Freshwater Snail		*								*										*
Indet. Hydrophilidae larvae	Water Beetle																	*			
Indet. Hydroptilidae pupa	Caddisfly		*																		
Indet. Isopoda (sea slater)	Sea Slater																			*	
Indet. *Limnephilus* sp.	Cadcisfly																		*		
Indet. Planariidae	Freshwater Flatworm																				
Indet. Planorbidae	Freshwater Snail	*																			
Ischnura elegans f. *infuscans* (adult)	Damselfly	*																			
Lestes sponsa	Damselfly			*						*										*	
Leuctra moselyi	Stonefly	*										*									

Table 5 – Macroinvertebrate species recorded and their distribution (cont.).

Scientific Name	Common Name	Woodland Park	Westhaugh	Sheardale	Pool of Muckart	Pike Ponds	Naemoor	Muckhart Mill	Inglewood	Gean	Foad (Old)	Foad (New)	Delph	Craigton	Castleton	Brucefield	Brandyhill	BDW (Small)	BDW (Large)	BDW (Existing)	Alva Ponds
Limnephilus rhombicus	Caddisfly	*										*									
Limnephilus vittatus	Caddisfly									*											
Lymnaea sp.	Freshwater Snail																				
Lymnaeidae	Freshwater Snail														*						*
Nemoura sp.	Stonefly																*				
Nemoura sp. prob. *N. cambrica*	Stonefly																*				
Nemoura sp. prob. *N. cinerea*	Stonefly	*													*						
Neomysis sp. prob. *N. integer*	Mysid Shrimp																	*	*		
Notonecta glauca	Backswimmer											*									*
Oecetis sp.	Caddisfly																				
Oligochaeta	Aquatic Worm	*				*	*	*		*	*	*	*	*	*	*	*				*
Omphiscola glabra	Freshwater Snail			*																	
Ostracoda	Seed Shrimp									*					*						
Phryganea bipunctata	Caddisfly											*									*
Physa sp.	Freshwater Snail	*				*															
Physa sp. poss. *P. fontinalis*	Freshwater Snail		*	*				*		*					*		*				
Pisidium / Sphaerium	Freshwater Cockle/ Pea Mussel														*						
Planorbarius corneus	Freshwater Snail														*						
Radix peregra	Freshwater Snail						*			*		*									*
Rhantus exsoletus	Water Beetle			*											*						
Sialis lutaria	Alderfly							*				*									
Sialis sp.	Alderfly						*		*							*					
Sigara concinna	Water Boatman						*		*									*	*	*	
Sigara distincta	Water Boatman						*									*					
Sigara dorsalis	Water Boatman						*														

Table 5 – Macroinvertebrate species recorded and their distribution (cont.).

Scientific Name	Common Name	Alva Ponds	BDW (Existing)	BDW (Large)	BDW (Small)	Brandyhill	Brucefield	Castleton	Craigton	Delph	Foad (New)	Foad (Old)	Gean	Inglewood	Muckhart Mill	Naemoor	Pike Ponds	Pool of Muckart	Sheardale	Westhaugh	Woodland Park
Sigara lateralis	Water Boatman		*	*	*				*					*		*					
Sigara sp.	Water Boatman										*										
Sigara sp. poss *S. limitata*	Water Boatman				*																
Sigara venusta	Water Boatman						*														
Sphaerium corneum	Freshwater Cockle						*				*										
Sympetrum striolatum	Dragonfly										*										
Tipulidae	Crane-fly											*									*
Triaenodes bicolor	Caddisfly																		*		

Table 6 – Miscellaneous records and their distribution.

Pond	Sedge Warbler (*Acrocephalus schoenobaenus*)	Small Tortoiseshell Butterfly (*Aglais urticae*)	Mallard (*Anas platyrhynchos*)	Ringlet (*Aphantopus hyperantus*)	Ringlet Butterfly (*Aphantopus hyperantus*)	Heron (*Ardea cinerea*)	Small Pearl-bordered Fritillary (*Boloria selene*)	Swan (*Cygnus olor*)	Common Blue Damselfly (*Enallagma cyathigerum*)	Kestrel (*Falco tinnunculus*)	Snipe (*Gallinago gallinago*)	Moorhen (*Gallinula chloropus*)	Three-spined Stickleback (*Gasterosteus aculeatus*)	Carpet Moth (Geometridae: Larentiinae)	Caddisfly (*Glyphotaelius* sp.)	Peacock Butterfly (*Inachis io*)	Blue tailed damselfly (*Ischnura elegans*)	Black-headed Gull (*Larus ridibundus*)	Emerald Damselfly (*Lestes sponsa*)	Small Copper (*Lycaena phlaeas*)	Meadow Brown (*Maniola jurtina*)	Noon-fly (*Mesembrina meridiana*)	Chimney sweeper (*Odezia atrata*)	Minnow (*Phoxinus phoxinus*)	Large White (*Pieris brassicae*)
Woodland Park																									
Westhaugh																									
Sheardale																									
Pool of Muckart																									
Pike Ponds				*			*		*				*								*		*		*
Naemoor				*																					
Muckhart Mill									*																
Inglewood			*	*				*	*				*				*				*				
Gean			*								*														
Foad (Old)				*			*																		
Foad (New)				*			*		*								*		*						
Delph			*																					*	
Craigton																									
Castleton				*					*						*		*		*						
Brucefield																									
Brandyhill				*																	*				
BDW (Small)											*		*	*		*					*		*		*
BDW (Large)						*		*	*	*															
BDW (Existing)		*			*			*									*	*							
Alva Ponds	*			*																	*				

Table 6 – Miscellaneous records and their distribution (cont.).

Scientific Name	Common Name	Alva Ponds	BDW (Existing)	BDW (Large)	BDW (Small)	Brandyhill	Brucefield	Castleton	Craigton	Delph	Foad (New)	Foad (Old)	Gean	Inglewood	Muckhart Mill	Naemoor	Pike Ponds	Pool of Muckart	Sheardale	Westhaugh	Woodland Park
Pieris napi	Green-veined White				*																
Pieris rapae	Small White	*												*							
Pyrrhosoma nymphula	Large Red Damselfly																*				
Rana temporaria	Frog	*																			
Sympetrum danae	Northern Darter																*				
Sympetrum striolatum	Common Darter																				
	Dragonflies										*										
Triturus sp. (juv.)	Newt						*	*	*		*								*		
Vanessa cardui	Painted Lady				*																
Various	Filamentous algae									*											

Reference

Biggs, J., Fox, G., Nicolet, P., Walker, D., Whitfield, M. and Williams, P., (1998). A Guide to the Methods of the National Pond Survey. Pond Action, Oxford (1998).

Campbell, L., (2003). Clackmannanshire Biodiversity Action Plan. *Clackmannanshire Biodiversity Partnership.*

Collinson, N.H., Biggs, J., Corfield, A., Hodson, M.J., Walker, D., Whitfield, M. and Williams, P.J., (1995). Temporary and permanent ponds: an assessment of the effects of drying out on the conservation value of aquatic macroinvertebrate communities. *Biological Conservation* 74, 125-133.

Doughty, C.R., (1989). A baseline study of acidified waters in Scotland. Research Contract PECD7/10/104, Department of the Environment. Glasgow: Clyde River Purification Board.

Lassiere, O., (1993). Central Region Lochs and Ponds: The Operation Brightwater survey of their status; past present and future. University of Stirling.

Macadam, C.R., (2005). Clackmannanshire's ponds – a hidden treasure. *Forth Naturalist and Historian.* Vol. 28, 21-23.

Palmer, M.A., (1989). A botanical classification of standing waters in Great Britain. *Research & Survey in Nature Conservation,* 19. Nature Conservancy Council, Peterborough.

Palmer, M.A., S.L. Bell and Butterfield I., (1992). A botanical classification of standing waters in Britain – applications for conservation and monitoring. *Aquatic Conservation – Marine and Freshwater Ecosystems* 2, No. 2, 125-143.

Pond Action, (2002). A guide to monitoring the ecological quality of ponds and canals using PSYM.

Smith, R.A.H., Stewart, N.F., Taylor, N.W. and Thomas, R.E., (1992). Checklist of the Plants of Perthshire. *Perthshire Society of Natural Science.*

Thiel, A. and Lindsay, H., (1999). Clackmannanshire Local Biodiversity Plan Habitat Audit.

Author Addresses

Malcolm Allan, 28 Kenilworth Road, Bridge of Allan FK9 4DU

Michael Bath, 6 Roman Road, Balfron G63 0PW

Mike Bell, 48 Newton Crescent, Dunblane FK15 0DZ

Neil Bielby, 56 Ochiltree, Dunblane FK15 0DF

Ken Dunn, 22 Livingstone Avenue, Callander FK17 8EP

John Harrison, 14a Abercrombie Place, Stirling FK8 2QP

Craig Macadam, Bradan Aquasurveys, 109 Johnston Avenue, Stenhousemuir FK5 4JY

Lorna Main, Stirling Council, Viewforth, Stirling FK8 2ET

David McVey, 39 Lochiel Drive, Milton of Campsie G66 8ET

Malcolm Shaw, 5 Pendreich Road, Bridge of Allan FK9 4LY

Andre Thiel, 6 Tait Place, Tillicoultry FK13 6RU

David Thorogood, 4 Archers Avenue, Stirling FK7 7RJ

FORTH AREA BIRD REPORT 2005

A.E. Thiel, M.V. Bell and N. Bielby

The present report is the 31st bird report for the Forth Valley (or Upper Forth) bird recording area. The report was written by Neil Bielby (Red-throated Diver to Coot, riverine passerines and WeBS/BBS comments in main list), Mike Bell (Oystercatcher to Razorbill) and Andre Thiel (Feral Pigeon to Reed Bunting and Escapees) with Cliff Henty contributing to the wader accounts. Cliff remains the Bird Recorder and all data should be sent to Cliff in the first instance.

The main part of the report consists of detailed species accounts presented in a systematic list. This is preceded by a summary of the main bird news from the past year and additional sections on the Breeding Bird Survey (BBS), the Wetland Bird Survey (WeBS), both written by Neil Bielby, and a Ringing Report, compiled by Andre Thiel. The bird report no longer contains a section on weather. A detailed account can, however, be found elsewhere in this volume.

ROUND-UP OF THE YEAR

The year started well with a 2nd winter Mediterranean Gull west of Airth on 2nd and 3rd January. This was followed by another 2nd winter bird at Powbridge near Throsk on 5th January. These may well have been the same bird as was present in Falkirk in late 2004 and thus be the fourth record for the recording area. The Raven roost at Doune continues to increase with 60 birds there on 7th January and 140 on 14th February. As last year, these increasing numbers were accompanied by an apparent spread from the core Callander-Doune-Dunblane area into south-east Stirlingshire, Clackmannanshire and Falkirk. A pair bred at Lake of Menteith and birds displaying over Mine Wood, Bridge of Allan, seem to indicate a slow consolidation of this expansion. Almost mirrored by the spread of Ravens was the ongoing apparent spread of Barn Owls into the same area. Clackmannanshire saw the same number of records in 2004 as in the preceding 25 years. Unfortunately there were also again a number of casualties of birds from both the local and neighbouring recording areas. The influx of Northern Bullfinches in 2004 was still apparent at the start of the year with stragglers in Doune on various dates in January and at Argaty on 21st February. Tree Sparrows continue to be reported from a wide range of locations from all three districts, both during the winter and during the breeding season. The largest flocks were 40 at both of the feeding stations near Thornhill in January. Overwintering waders in the form of Green Sandpiper on the Teith and Carron on 23rd January and at Gart gravel pit on 5th February, Ruff at Skinflats on 6th February, Spotted Redshank at Blackness on 20th February and Greenshanks at Blackness on 26th January and 27th February and at Skinflats to 24th March provided a bit of diversity during the winter.

A male Black Redstart was present near Earl's Hill on 23rd March – only the fourth record for the recording area. Two days later a Greenfinch that had been ringed at Wick in the Highlands was recaptured in Menstrie, a distance of 259 km. A Great Grey Shrike was seen at L. Venachar on 4th April.

Spring started with the arrival of the first Greenshank at Blackness on 2nd, Kinneil on 3rd and Skinflats on 11th April. There was a scattering of Green Sandpipers at various sites in Falkirk during April. This was followed by a Whimbrel at Skinflats on 19th April. Our local Black-tailed Godwits seem to have developed a similar urge to migrate, albeit at a smaller scale. They are less faithful than in the past to Skinflats and Kinneil and are inceasingly found upstream in the Cambus area where 5 were present on 21st April. A day later a Nuthatch was spotted in the same garden in Alva as the very first bird for the recording area in 1999. Other birds in Balquhidder on 22nd May and in Dunblane on 26th may indicate that birds have arrived in our area for good; the first confirmation of breeding is eagerly anticipated. A Whimbrel was at Kippen on 26th April and again 27th May.

May started with an unseasonal 1st summer Iceland Gull at Skinflats on 12th to 13th May. Hot on the heels there was an Avocet between 14th to 17th May. This is the second year in a row that Avocets stopped over at Skinflats. The site confirmed its premier position as a migration location with a 1st summer Little Gull on 22nd May. Two Dotterel on Ben Ledi on 28th May was a good sighting.

An interesting record came from Cambusmore/Gart gravel pit where a pair of Little Ringed Plovers were seen displaying on 2nd June with a bird apparently on a nest on 22nd June. This is only the second breeding record for our area. Kinneil came into its own with the second Iceland Gull of the year (a 2nd summer bird) on 9th June and subsequently on various dates in July, August and September. An interesting recovery of a female Siskin killed by a cat in Strathyre was made on 20th June. The bird had been ringed in France. In July a male Common Rosefinch was recorded again in the same general northern area as in previous years.

Wader return migration started at Skinflats with a Greenshank on 30th June and built up to 8 birds there by August. This was followed by the first of a handful of Whimbrel at Kinneil on 23rd July. The first returning Green Sandpiper was recorded at Carronshore on 13th August.

Local autumn passage of scarce waders was confined to a handful of records. Up to 5 Curlew Sandpipers were present in the Grangemouth area between 1st and 18th September and two Little Stints at Skinflats on 4th September. Skua passage was equally poor, the first Arctic Skua passing Skinflats on 9th September.

Probably the highlight of the year was the discovery of a 2nd winter/sub-adult Ring-billed Gull at Kinneil on 16th September. The bird stayed until 1st November and represents the first record for the recording area. This was followed by another Mediterranean Gull (winter-plumaged bird) there on 12th

November, representing the fifth record for the area.

As at the start of the year, some diversity was provided by overwintering waders. A Greenshank was wintering at Skinflats from 3rd November to the end of the year with two birds together there on three dates in November. Two Green Sandpipers also stayed the winter and were seen at Carronshore on 31st December.

Conservationwise there have unfortunately also been a number of less pleasing developments. Up to a few years ago Lecropt had the largest wintering flocks of Tree Sparrow and Yellowhammer in the area as well as large flocks of finches, thrushes, Skylarks and Pink-footed Geese, attracted by the mix of cereal and oilseed stubbles, grass and mature hedgerows. A change of tenant led to the removal/severe cutting back of several hedgerows and the spraying of two large grass fields with herbicides. This has led over the last two years to a large decline in wintering birds. At Cambus Pools shooting and motorcycle racing seem to have become more common again in recent years with a predicted disturbance on birds. Motorcycles were also a problem at Skinflat pools in the autumn.

RECORD SUBMISSION

Annual Bird Reports depend largely on contributions from the local birdwatching community. As far as possible these are acknowledged with initials with a full list of contributors included at the start of the report. More contributors than ever (115) have sent in data this year. There is not surprisingly an ever increasing amount of data reaching the editors in various formats. To facilitate the preparation of the report, contributors are strongly encouraged to submit their data as soon as possible after the end of the year. Electronic files are much the preferred format and a standard spreadsheet is available from Cliff Henty. Thanks are due to those contributors who are now submitting their data in this format.

Several observers send in a list largely or entirely for their home locality. Much of this information is not appropriate for inclusion in these annual reports but it is valuable to have on record (e.g. for conservation action). These are kept in a special file. At the moment there are fifteen such lists referring to the whole district from Falkirk to Killin. Several contributors send in data, often of common species, from repeated visits to the same locality. This is useful, as it provides a better picture of bird occupancy than data from single visits.

Following on from last year, an increasing number of records are submitted with 6-figure grid references. Also more contributors add the name of the nearest village. This is most appreciated, as it enormously speeds up cross-checks and is a valuable resource for conservation action.

The sparse information available about common breeding species is improved by data from the Breeding Bird Survey (BBS). For less common species data can sometimes be summarised in terms of the numbers of pairs or apparently occupied territories for particular locations. The organisers for both the estuary and the inland waters parts of the national wildfowl counts (WeBS) have made available the results for this report. These often contribute to the species accounts and there is also a separate summary for inland waters which concentrates on localities.

For many species the records sent in are very unrepresentative of their general distribution. This applies particularly to very common species or to those that are secretive or breed in inaccessible locations. The status of species is detailed in a Check List, published in the Forth Naturalist and Historian, Vol 15. Additional information along with guidelines for the submission of records can be obtained from N. Bielby, 56 Ochiltree, Dunblane, FK15 0DF. 01786 823830. neil.bielby@tiscali.co.uk. In addition there is a coded summary of general distribution after the species name. This often apparently contradicts the detailed records that are published for the year. The codes are thus:

B - Breeding status: widespread (present in more than five 10 km squares)
b   "   "   :   local , scarce (present in fewer than five 10 km squares)
W - Winter status: widespread or often in groups of more than ten
w -   "   "   :   local, scarce (local and usually fewer than ten in a group)
P :   Passage (used when species is usually absent in winter; P or p used for widespread or local as in winter status)
S or s :   Summer visitor (used for species present in summer but which do not normally breed; S or s used for widespread or local as in winter status).

Thus BW would be appropriate for Robin, B for Swallow, p for Ruff and SW for Cormorant. No status letter is used if a species occurs less than every other year.

An asterisk (*) in front of the species name means that all records received for scarce species have been quoted. The SOC has pressed for a more systematic vetting of records of species that are unusual locally. Our area has an informal panel of five members: C. Henty (Recorder), A. Smith, D. Orr-Ewing, A. Blair and D. Thorogood. We have produced a list of species that are scarce locally and where the records need to be supported by either a full description or sufficient evidence to remove any reasonable doubt. The list will be available from Cliff Henty. Any species which is a vagrant to the area and some of those which are asterisked in this report will come into this category. The judging of Scottish or national rarities continues as before and descriptions need to be submitted to the relevant committees. Observers should be aware that aberrant individuals of common species of birds appear quite regularly and these sometimes resemble rarities. There is also the problem of escaped birds and of hybridisation, a particular problem in captive wildfowl which may then appear in natural situations.

The British Ornithologists' Union (BOU) has appealed that introduced/escaped species be recorded locally. As the published information on these species is not necessarily complete, self-sustaining populations of such species may exist which are not known or adequately recorded. The BOU therefore encourages observers to record and monitor all naturalized species (particularly but not exclusively breeding records and interactions with native species) and escaped species seen in the wild to assist it to make future recommendations for Category C status, if a self-sustaining naturalized population is established.

The following abbreviations have been used : Ad(s). - adult(s), AoT - apparently occupied territory, b/lkm - birds per linear kilometre, Br. - bridge, BoA - Bridge of Allan, c/n - clutch of n eggs, conf. - confluence, BBS - Breeding Bird Survey, CP - Country Park, E - east, Est. - estuary, Fm. - farm, F - Female, G. - Glen, GP - gravel pit, Imm. - immature, incl. - including, Juv - juvenile, L. - Loch, N - north, NR - Nature Reserve, M - Male, Max. - maximum, ON - on nest, Res - Reservoir, R. - river, Rd - road, S - south, SP - summer plumage, W - west, WeBS - Wetland Bird Survey, Y - young, , > flying/flew.

The area covered by the report comprises the council areas of Falkirk and Clackmannan together with Stirling, excluding Loch Lomondside and other parts of the Clyde drainage basin. Please note that we do not include the Endrick water, i.e. Fintry and Balfron. Records from Carron Valley Reservoir are published here but it is proposed that Clyde should cover all the forest south of the reservoir.

CONTRIBUTORS

This report has been compiled from records submitted by the contributors listed below. Where no initials are given in brackets, contributors participated in targeted surveys (e.g. WeBS) but did not additionally submit data to the systematic list. For some contributors who sent their data to particular schemes (e.g. Birdtrack), the full names are not available and their contributions are listed as 'BTO'.

D. Anderson (DA), M. Anderson (MA), P. Ashworth (PMA), S. Ashworth (SA), M. Avery (MAV), A. Ayre, B. Barker (BB), Bean Goose Action Group (BGAG), M. Bell (MVB), N. Bielby (NB), Bird News Services (BNS), A. Blair (AB), L. Bowser (LB), R. Broad (RAB), A.&L. Brown (ALB), BTO, R. Bullman (RB), J. Calladine (JC), D. Cameron (DJC), G. Cannon (GC), I. Carmichael, P. Carter (PGC), D. Chamberlain (DC), R. Chapman (RC), D.&A. Christie (DAC), N. Clark (NDC), K. Conlin (KC), S. Cooper, R. Cowen (RC), T. Craig (TC), R. Dalziel (RDZ), R.&H. Dawson (RHD), R. Downie (RD), D. Egerton (DE), K. Egerton (KE), T. Findlay (TF), S. Forbes (SF), G. Fraser (GF), K. Freeman (KF), J. Fulton (JF), J. Gallacher (JG), M. Given (MG), R. Gooch (RLG), J. Grainger (JG), R. Griffiths (RG), A. Hannah (AH), C. Hemple (CH), I. Henderson, C. Henty (CJH), D. Holland (DH), P. Hyvonen (PH), L. Ingram (LI), D. Jones (DJ), J. Kaye (JK), E. Keenan (EK), I. Keenan (IK), D. Kerr (DK), R. Knight, M. Kobs (MK), D. Land (DL), A. Lauder (AL), P. Lee, G.&E. Leisk (GEL), P. Lubbers (PAL), M. Maclean (MML), I. Madden, C.J. Mallett (CJM), D. Matthews (DM), P. May (PM), M. McCartney (MM), M. McDonnell (MMcD), B. McGowan (BMcG), R. McKenzie (RMcK), G. McShane (GM), G. Mercer (JM),

Mugdock Country Park Rangers, M. Mylne (MMy), J. Nimmo (JN), L. Nisbett (LN), M. O'Brien (MO), C. Oldham (CO), D. Orr-Ewing (DOE), B. Osborn (BO), G. Owens (GO), E.&J. Payne, D. Pickett (DWP), K. Pilkington (KP), D. Redwood, R. Ridley (RR), D. Robertson (DRO), A. Rogers (ACR), T. Rogers (TR), A. Samson (ASM), the late P. Sandeman (PWS), M. Scott, S.&R. Sexton (SRS), R. Shand (RS), J. Shanks (JS), D. Shenton, H. Simpson (HS), A. Smith (AS), K. Smith (KS), E. Smy (ES), C. Spray (CS), Stirling District Ranger Service (SDRS), R. Theakston (RT), A. Thiel (AET), D. Thorogood (DT), J. Towill (JT), N. Trout (NT), M. Trubridge (MT), C. Waddell (CW), A. Wallace (ASW), A. Watterson (AEW), H. Weir, C. Wernham, M. White (MW), N. White (NDW), A. Whittington (AEWh), K. Wilkinson (KW), J. Willett (JW), P. Wills (PW), K. Wilson (KWI), L. Winskill, S. Zisman (SZ).

Thanks are due to D. Orr-Ewing for RSPB data on Red Kites and Ospreys and to S. Zisman for data from the Central Scotland Black Grouse and Capercaillie Group (CSBGCG).

BREEDING BIRD SURVEY (BBS)

This report describes the results of the Breeding Bird Survey, which is organised in our area by Neil Bielby. The primary aim of this survey, run by the British Trust for Ornithology (BTO), is to provide population trends for a range of common and widespread bird species in the UK. Survey plots based on 1-km squares of the National Grid are selected randomly with the aim of surveying the same squares each year.

Thirty out of the 42 squares allocated to our area were surveyed in 2005. This was two less than last year. The area covered by the BTO's 'Central Region' corresponds roughly to that of the Upper Forth Bird Reporting Area within the old Central Region, plus an area of Perth and Kinross stretching as far as Glen Devon to the east and Glen Artney to the north.

For analysis purposes, the squares or parts of squares, have been allocated to four broad habitat groups. Habitat detail for the area covered by the BTO's 'Central Region' is not available but it is for the old local government area of that name and a comparison between this and the BBS coverage in 2005 is detailed below.

	BBS 2005	Full take up	LG 'CR'	Species	B/LKM
Mountain and Moorland (A)	28 %	37 %	49 %	43	34.8
Conifer woodland / edge (B)	14 %	13 %	13 %	44	53.3
Farmland (C)	48 %	37 %	34 %	84	88.2
Urban/suburban (D)	10 %	13 %	4 %	43	112

As the habitat comparison above shows, Mountain and Moorland was even more under-represented than usual when compared to the local government figures, with Farmland and Urban/Suburban over-represented. Of the squares not surveyed, 6 were type A, 3 type B and 5 type C. This means that even if all the issued squares were surveyed, mountain and moorland habitats would still be under-represented. Overall, 97 species were recorded, a new high and 4 more than in 2004, despite coverage being lower. Barn Owl was recorded for the first time, making a total of 117 species that have been recorded during the 10 years the survey has taken place. The average number of birds per linear km (b/lkm) was 71.9, the second highest to date and 5 % above the average, some 23 % above that of 2004 (probably due to the low percentage of upland squares surveyed).

Starling was again the most numerous species recorded, although this year it had to share top spot with Carrion Crow. Rook was third with Chaffinch dropping down a place to fourth. Meadow Pipit, Woodpigeon and Jackdaw followed. It should be noted that these figures are influenced by detectability, which often dictates which species are recorded in the greatest numbers.

Habitat comparison

It should be noted that, because the habitat divisions are so broad, small areas of almost any habitat (and the birds therein) can occur in any other habitat.

(A) Mountain and Moorland

Results from 11 squares containing some of this habitat were received in 2005. Thirty-two linear km were perambulated, slightly below the average. No doubt because of this, the number of species recorded, 43, was the lowest in 4 years, although the number of birds per linear kilometre was the highest to date at 32.8.

Unsurprisingly, Meadow Pipit is the most abundant species found in this habitat with 13.4 b/lkm recorded, a little above the mean. Carrion Crow was 2nd with 11 b/lkm, the highest yet, almost 3 times the average. Skylark was the only other species recorded at more than 1 b/lkm with a rate of 2.7, the 2nd lowest in 8 years. Snipe, Curlew, Skylark, Meadow Pipit, Stonechat, Wheatear, Mistle Thrush, Carrion Crow and Reed Bunting were recorded at their highest densities, whilst Red Kite, Red Grouse, Golden Plover, Whinchat and Raven were restricted to this habitat.

Conifer Woodland and Moorland/Conifer edge

Large areas of upland Scotland have been planted with exotic conifers since the First World War. In 1995 they covered 12.8 % of Central Region; BBS coverage of this habitat in 2005 was 14 %. Because of the dense nature of these plantations, surveyors are inclined to route their transects either along natural breaks in the planting or along the outside edge of the plantation, for this reason, the two habitats have been combined. The altitude of this habitat ranged from 70 m to 300 m asl.

The number of species recorded was 44, the same as the previous year which also equals the mean, whilst the 53.3 b/lkm was slightly above average. The most common species was again Chaffinch at 9.2 b/lkm followed by Goldcrest at 6.1 b/lkm – the highest rate to date and over twice the mean. Coal

Tit was also recorded at its highest ever rate, 5.2 b/lkm – twice the mean. Species recorded at their highest frequency in this habitat were Sparrowhawk, Cuckoo, Wren, Song Thrush, Blackcap, Willow Warbler, Goldcrest, Coal Tit, Treecreeper, Jay, Chaffinch, Siskin, Linnet, Lesser Redpoll and Bullfinch. Only Crossbill was restricted to this habitat.

Farmland

Coverage of this habitat increased from 44 % to 48 % in 2005, 14 % above the 34 % of the former Central Region. The squares are well spread around the area and cover various farming types. They also take in broad leaved and mixed woodland, which, at 2.3 % and 2.5 % of the land area respectively, are not adequately represented by the present coverage to be treated as separate habitats. Altitude of the squares ranges from sea level to 180 m.

The number of species recorded was 84, 3 above the 8-year mean of 81. Yet again, the most numerous of these was Starling at 8.5 b/lkm followed by Rook at 8.2, Chaffinch at 5.8 with Carrion Crow and Woodpigeon at 5.4. Amongst species recording their highest frequency in this habitat were Buzzard, Pheasant, Oystercatcher, Woodpigeon, Swallow, House Martin, Pied Wagtail, Blue Tit, Great Tit and Goldfinch. Species restricted to this habitat included Grey Partridge, Lapwing, Grasshopper Warbler, Spotted Flycatcher, Long-tailed Tit and Tree Sparrow.

Urban/Suburban

Ten percent of BBS squares cover this habitat, over double the actual. The 43 species recorded was the highest to date and as usual, the highest number of b/lkm was found here with 112. The 11.6 linear km traversed was also the most so far.

Generalist species yet again topped the abundancy list for this habitat with Starling recorded at 21.2 b/lkm, Rook at 13.2, Jackdaw at 9.2, Feral Pigeon at 8.2, Lesser Black-backed Gull at 8, Blackbird at 6.8 and House Sparrow at 5.7. Species recorded at their highest density in this habitat were Lesser Black-backed Gull, Feral Pigeon, Collared Dove, Swift, Dunnock, Blackbird, Whitethroat, Chiffchaff, Magpie, Jackdaw, Rook, Starling, House Sparrow and Greenfinch. There were no species found in this and no other habitat.

WETLAND BIRD SURVEY (WeBS)

WeBS is a monthly waterfowl census organised under the auspices of the BTO (British Trust for Ornithology). The core months are September to March inclusive. For this report 'waterfowl' includes divers, grebes, cormorants, herons, swans, geese (excluding Pink-footed and Greylag for which WWT (Wildfowl and Wetlands Trust) organises separate counts), ducks, sawbills, rails, gallinules and coots. Waders, gulls, and Kingfisher numbers are also collected. Locally, we also record raptors, Dipper and Grey Wagtail.

Although the WeBS scheme was only officially launched in October 1993, it continues the traditions of two long running count schemes which had monitored waterfowl numbers in the UK since 1947. Counts in the area covered by this report only go back as far as the winter of 1960-1. When interpreting the various statistics in this report, please bear in mind that Coot and Great Crested Grebe were not counted until 1982-3, Little Grebe until 1985-6 and Cormorants until 1986-7. The three categories of Mallard in the tables also require explanation. Mallard (i) are totally wild receiving no human assistance; Mallard (ii) are wild but are assisted in some way by humans, i.e. duck pond birds fed by the public or birds fed by wildfowlers to attract them to flight ponds for shooting; Mallard (iii) owe their existence to humans, being reared by them, released onto shooting ponds and fed for their brief lives.

This report covers the area occupied by the new local government councils of Stirling, Falkirk and Clackmannanshire. As this area is identical to that covered by the now defunct Central Region, the latter title has been retained both for continuity and convenience, hereafter referred to as the 'region'.

By the end of July 2006, forms for 102 still water sites, 119.7 km of river and 20.2 km of canal had been received from 47 counters who made 545 individual counts of still water sites and walked 820 km of river and canal bank through the winter. A total of 44843 waterfowl were recorded with 30302 (69 %) found on still waters and 14541 (31 %) on linear water features.

Waterfowl Facts and Figures

Still Water Sites

Standing water in Central Region amounts to 7693 hectares or 2.92 % of the area. The steep rainfall gradient from the NW to the SE of the region is illustrated by the fact that L. Katrine has an average 2500 mm of rain a year compared to Grangemouth with 890 mm. All the major sites were counted this winter but the following sites, whose historical monthly mean counts vary between 13 – 66 birds, either weren't counted or their forms have yet to be returned: Ashfield Pools (13); Balvag Marshes (28); Flanders Moss Lochan (36); Waltersmuir Woods Res. (40); Hutchinson Loch (44) and L. Macanrie (66). The table below shows waterfowl numbers from matched counts at the top 20 still sites and 4 main river sites (sites with MA ii and iii have been excluded). This probably gives the truest indication of overall trends.

	Ave. 94/95-99/00	2000/1	2001/2	2002/3	2003/4	2004/5	2005/6	Ave. of 12 winters
September	2461	2110	2180	2633	2437	2407	2029	2400
October	3641	3016	2934	3519	3524	3330	2610	3394
November	4185	4565	4129	4526	3957	4213	3797	4180
December	4768	4831	3758	4124	3911	4571	3697	4498
January	4507	4419	3418	4234	4139	4840	3762	4353
February	3999	3761	4274	3467	4022	3566	3559	3919
March	2446	2478	2512	2432	2683	2778	2670	2539
Totals	26104	25180	23205	24935	24673	25705	22124	25284

This winter produced the lowest totals in 12 years of comprehensive counts, 12 % below the mean. Every month, apart from March, was below average with December showing a deficit of 18 %. However, this drop in numbers coincides with the lowest ever average for monthly counts at Gartmorn Dam. The latter were 463 (63 %) below the mean of the previous eleven winters which, when multiplied by the number of months counted (7), gives 3241 – very similar to the 3447 which is the difference between this winter's total in the table above and the mean total of the previous eleven winters. Over the previous eleven winters, Gartmorn Dam accounted, on average, for 19 % of the totals in the above tables, whereas this winter, it accounted for only 8 %. That this winter's low numbers are mostly attributable to the drastically reduced numbers at Gartmorn Dam is further reinforced in that, the remaining sites used in the compilation of the above table, show a drop of only 2 % on their combined mean of the previous eleven years. To complicate matters, a new counter took over Gartmorn Dam this winter. As even the most experienced of counters takes quite a while to become acquainted with a new site, especially one as complicated as this, interpreting the large drop in numbers this year should be done with extreme caution. Note that peak mid-winter numbers are almost double those of September, illustrating the importance of our area for wintering waterfowl.

Turning to individual sites, the top ten along with monthly averages are listed below. (previous seasons figures in brackets)

Pos	Site	Average	Pos	Site	Average
1. (2)	Lake of Menteith	447 (616)	6. (17)	Lochs Dochart / Iubhair	224 (93)
2. (5)	L. Earn	328 (227)	7. (8)	L. Venachar	202 (140)
3. (3)	Cambusmore / Gart GP	324 (336)	8. (6)	Killin Marshes	190 (167)
4. (4)	Airthrey Loch	291 (272)	9. (7)	Vale of Coustry	177 (148)
5. (1)	Gartmorn Dam	268 (732)	10. (23)	Skinflats Pools	159 (66)

(The above table excludes sites where mallard are reared and released for shooting.)

With Gartmorn Dam's poor showing the Lake of Menteith takes over top spot, even though numbers were down 27 % on the previous winter's record counts. (still 33 % above the long term average (LTA) though). Numbers at L. Earn were up 44 % on the previous winter and 23 % on the LTA, enough to promote this site to its highest ever position of 2nd. Cambusmore/Gart GP retained 3rd spot although numbers were down slightly on both the 2004/5 winter and the LTA It is remarkable how the ever changing topography of this site, and disturbance as extraction continues apace, has so little affect on both the birds and their numbers. The position of Airthrey Loch also remained unchanged, with numbers up 7 % on the previous winter, only 1 below the LTA With an average count 63 % below those of 2004/5 and 69 % down on the L.T.A, it comes as no surprise that Gartmorn Dam falls to its lowest ever league position. Bird numbers at Lochs Dochart and Iubhair are regularly adversely affected by both ice cover and flooding. Unlike the previous winter, neither of these events coincided with counts in 2005/6, resulting in numbers increasing by 140 %. These were also 42 % above the LTA which allowed the site to claim 6th place, 3 above its mean. L. Venachar also enjoyed a good winter, with counts up 44 % and 38 % on 2004/5 and the LTA respectively, it moved up one place to 7th. Despite recording its highest ever average, 90 % above the LTA, Killin Marshes dropped 2 places to 8th. Another site to drop 2 places despite recording higher numbers than the previous season was Vale of Coustry. The final place in the above table goes to Skinflats Pools, which appears in the top ten for the first time and whose average is the highest for the site to date, up 140 % and 156 % on 2004/5 and the LTA respectively.

Turning to the less populated sites, Black Loch, Slamannan; St Helen's Loch, Bonnybridge and Little Denny Resr. in Falkirk District all had good winters with monthly averages at the top end of their seasonal range, around double the mean. Numbers also continue to climb annually at the old opencast mining site of Greencraig Ponds, Avonbridge. The redundant curling pond at Kinneil House was counted for the first time, returning a healthy average of 59 birds per month, putting it in 22nd place. Several public 'duck' ponds have shown a marked decline in the past couple of years with numbers only half those of the mean; people don't appear to be feeding them less, so is some other factor responsible, ie. disease? Although no dead birds have been reported.

In Clackmannanshire, the pond at Boll Farm, Alva was also counted for the first time. The owners put out grain which attracts Mute Swans, often over 20 birds are present. As there are several ringing schemes for this bird, both in and furth of Scotland, it provides an excellent opportunity to monitor the species. Kersiepow South Pond had its second poorest winter with counts down 30 % on the mean whilst the 'Alva floods' have been virtually deserted the past two winters. By contrast, Blackdevonmouth Marshes enjoyed their best season to date with numbers up 1.5 times on the mean at 43 birds per month.

Overall numbers from the 11 sites counted in the Clyde drainage area have remained remarkably consistent over the years. However, returns from individual sites do vary from winter to winter. This time, numbers at Dumbrock Loch were 3 times the mean whilst Craigallian and Ardinning Lochs had only half the usual. The first two of these sites, along with Deil's Craig Dam and Mill Dam, Milndavie recorded their hundredth WeBS counts in 2005/6.

In the hills to the south of the Carse of Stirling, the Touch and Buckieburn reservoirs received their first counts in three winters whilst numbers at nearby

L. Coulter were the second highest on record, twice the LTA In sharp contrast, Carron Valley Resr. continues to hold low numbers of birds, this winter's monthly average being only 32 % of the LTA Loch Laggan and Kippen Muir Dam also received their hundredth count during the winter but numbers were again depressed at roughly half the mean.

Of the small lochans on the south side of the Teith between Callander and Doune; L. Watston returned its 2nd poorest numbers in its long history of counts with an average of only 54 birds, some 36 % below the mean. Whilst Upper Lanrick Dam also fared badly, with numbers down 68 %, the relatively recently created Torrie Lochan saw numbers up 64 %.

North of the Highland Line (just), L. Rusky continues to improve, the monthly average count of 50 being the highest yet, 80 % above the mean. Despite the disturbance caused by the construction of the wind farm on the Braes of Doune, L. Mahaick had its best winter since 1986/7 with an average of 130 birds a month; almost double the LTA Numbers at Lochs Voil/Doine were maintained at the recent high level, over twice the mean whilst at Glen Finglas Resr. they were up by 62 %. Numbers at the wild and remote oligotrophic L. Arklet were also double the norm but at L. Ard, they were half the average, similar to the previous time this site was counted.

Absolute numbers are only one indication of a sites importance; species diversity is a major factor as well. All the species we record locally on WeBS are included here: Skinflats Pools recorded the greatest diversity with 34 species followed by Cambusmore/Gart GP with 30, then the Lake of Menteith with 28 and Carron Valley Resr. with 25 – despite its low abundancy. L. Watston is another site where, although overall numbers were depressed this winter, the number of species, 24, was the 5th highest. The 4th site in the abundancy league, Airthrey Loch, only had 12 species, fewer than Alva Floods (13) which only averaged 6 wildfowl a visit.

Linear Water Features: Rivers and Canals

The 119.7 km of river counted at least once this winter was the 2nd highest in the eleven years this type of habitat has been covered by WeBS locally, some 18 % above the mean. The 695 km of river bank perambulated during this winter was the most to date. A new section of the R. Forth, from Offrins of Gartur (on the edge of Gartrenich Moss) to Cardross Bridge, was counted for the first time.

Season average in birds per linear kilometre river									
	1996/7	1997/8	1998/9	1999/0	2000/1	2001/2	2002/3	2003/4	2004/5	2005/6
Allan Water	3.7	7.1	14.2	12.2	12.0	10.6	10.6	12.3	9.8	10.7
R. Carron	10.4	11.2	12.6	13.4	13.1	15.1	18.8	22.1	14.6	18.6
R. Devon	11.2	8.3	9.5	15.0	15.2	15.1	17.2	17.2	17.4	14.8
R. Forth	17.8	14.1	15.5	19.0	17.0	23.4	27.7	14.4	13.9	17.5
R. Teith	22.7	16.0	8.9	22.1	17.2	36.6	25.5	35.6	18.4	37.2
Edrick Water	34.1	58.9	50.4	79.2	36.5	-	-	31.6	27.5	25.8
Union Canal	4.38	6.09	7.21	6.92	5.81	3.93	2.19	2.59	1.43	2.24
F & C Canal	7.22	7.36	8.84	7.88	5	6.33	5.85	7.33	9.97	14.38
Overall	**13.8**	**11.8**	**13.5**	**16.4**	**14.1**	**16.1**	**17.5**	**16.6**	**13.1**	**14.0**

The R. Forth was counted from Offrins of Gartur down to Fallin (where the estuary counts take over), a distance of some 64 km. The R. Devon was counted from Dollar down to the R. Forth with the R. Carron covered from the M876 by Denny down to the A905 at Grangemouth where again, the estuary counts take over. The Allan Water was covered from the Perth and Kinross Council boundary down to Dunblane and from Bridge of Allan to the R. Forth. (the section between Dunblane and Bridge of Allan is not only difficult to access but also holds few birds). The Endrick is counted from Killearn to the Dumbarton Council boundary. Coverage was disappointing on the R. Teith with only the section through Callander and the stretch from Doune Bridge to Wester Row covered. Between Callander and Doune Bridge the river is fast flowing and contains few birds but that portion from Wester Row to the R. Forth confluence has been shown to hold good numbers of birds in the past.

The only portion of canal in the region not covered was the stretch of the Forth and Clyde between Bonnybridge and Banknock but again, past experience indicates that few birds are present.

The Allan Water and Rivers Carron, Devon and Forth all returned numbers of waterfowl within their annual ranges. The high figure for the R. Teith is heavily disproportionably influenced by the public fed Mallard at the Meadows in Callander. The lower numbers on the Endrick Water since 2003/4 are due to the section from Killearn to Drymen Bridge only being counted since then. Numbers on the Union Canal still have not recovered since the restoration work whilst those on the Forth and Clyde Canal were at their highest ever.

More details of individual species can be found in the systematic list below.

RINGING REPORT

This is the second full ringing report. The following section lists all ringed birds seen in the recording area during the year. Contributors are encouraged to report colour-ringed wildfowl to the relevant organisers and/or the BTO and not to assume that somebody else has already done so, as all movements are of interest to the ringers and add to our understanding of bird ecology and migration patterns. Thanks are due to Allan and Lyndesay Brown, Les Hatton and Shirley Millar (Tay Ringing Group), Christie Hemple and Bob Swann for making available data on movements of birds seen in the recording area.

A total of 50 recoveries (excluding multiple sightings of the same bird) were made in 2005. Most are, not surprisingly, of Greylag Geese (8) and Mute Swans (23). Others related to Greenfinch (3), Whooper Swan (2), Barn Owl (2) and one each for Shelduck, Curlew, Woodpigeon, Waxwing, Blackbird, Pied Flycatcher, Chaffinch and Siskin.

There were a number of interesting recoveries. A Greylag Goose ringed in Iceland has been seen on several occasions in Clackmannanshire in both 2004 and 2005. Two Whooper Swans, also ringed in Iceland, were seen in Menstrie and at L. Iubhair, respectively. A Mute Swan – a species known for avoiding travelling long distances – ringed in Northumberland made it to Airthrey Loch, BoA. A Curlew ringed in the Netherlands was seen at Kinneil and a Siskin ringed in France was killed by a cat in Strathyre.

During 2005 the Tay Ringing Group ringed a total of 1,801 birds of 44 species in Central Region. The most frequent species that were ringed were Great Tit (506), Blue Tit (366), Swallow (133) and Pied Flycatcher (99). Species of conservation interest included Barn Owl (4 fully grown birds and 12 pulli), Song Thrush (9 fully grown, 4 pulli), Grasshopper Warbler (3 fully grown), Spotted Flycatcher (5 fully grown), Starling (2 pulli), Tree Sparrow (1 fully grown), Bullfinch (15 fully grown) and Reed Bunting (6 fully grown).

Christie Hemple ringed 11 Mute Swans in the recording area. Allan and Lyndesay Brown, who are ringing Mute Swans in Fife and the Lothians, are particularly keen to learn if any of the birds ringed by them (green or white Darvic rings) breed outside their study area.

Recoveries are listed in Voous order, as for the systematic list, under the following headings:

Ring number   **Date & Location seen in 2005**   Location ringed
                                                            Date ringed   Observer
followed by the location(s) where the bird was seen in between.

GREYLAG GOOSE
Grey neck BZV   4 Jan N of Kersiepow, Alva   Masvatn, S-Ping, ICELAND
                                                          15 Nov 1999   AET
                     9, 16 Jan E of Alva Ind. Estate
                     13 Feb Midtown, Blackgrange
                     22 Feb Sheriffyards, Gartmorn Dam
This bird spent most of its winter visits between 1997 and 2003 in Fife. It was first recorded in the Forth Area in February 2004 and has since been recorded repeatedly in Clackmannanshire with occasional sightings in Fife. Further details of movements can be found in the 2004 bird report.
Grey neck DPS   **22 Jan Haugh Cottage, Cambus**   Loch Eye (Easter Ross)
                                                          13 Oct 1998   AET
Kintrae nr. Elgin 17 Nov 1998; Kirkton nr. Elgin 29 Nov 1998; Fairness, Comrie (Tayside) 9 Jan 1999; Rothiemoon Fm., Nethy Bridge 27 Nov 1999; Baddan, nr. Golspie 25 Oct 2001; Cuthill, Dornoch 4 Nov 2001; Bullechach (Caithness) 5 Dec 2001; Messigate, Tankerness (Orkney) 1 and 5 Nov 2004.

Grey neck HCA   4, 5, 9, 10 and 16 Jan West Alva   Loch Eye (Easter Ross)

		24 Feb 2000 AET
	4 Jan Kersiepow	NB
	22 Jan Haugh Cottage, Cambus	AET
	15 Mar East Gogar	NB
	16 Mar East Gogar	AET

Following sightings nr. Montrose (Angus) and in Iceland in 2001, this bird has been seen repeatedly in the recording area, especially Clackmannanshire, since January 2003. Further details of movements can be found in the 2004 bird report.

Grey neck XD   20 Nov 2004 S of Alva Ind. Estate   Loch Eye (Easter Ross)

                                                    14 Apr 1996   AET

        24 Dec 2004 Haugh Cottage, Cambus

Kilwhiss (Fife) 5 Nov 1998; Lazyfold, Duncanston (Aberdeenshire) 10 Nov 1999; Haugh of Blackgrange, Cambus (Clackmannanshire) 18 Nov 2003.

Orange neck BIV   7 Feb Dochart Haughs East   Loch Eye (Easter Ross)

                                                    7 Nov 2004   NB

Red neck ABU   28 Dec W of Drymen Bridge   Lintrathen Loch (Tayside)

                                                    30 Nov 2003   AET

This is the only sighting of this bird since it was ringed.

Red leg AJA   17 Dec W 2004, E of Alva Ind. Estate   Nosterfield

                                                    2 Mar 2003   AET

Giffordtown (Fife) 29 Dec 2004; St. Cloud (Grampian) 31 Oct 2004

White leg TB   13 Feb Midtown, Blackgrange   Loch Eye (Easter Ross)

                                                    23 Oct 1993   AET

Summerton, Glasgow 5 Feb 1994; Hunterston (Ayrshire) 13 Mar 1994

SHELDUCK

White leg 1 GN17975   18 Sep Alloa Inch   Coble Shore, Eden Estuary

                                                    12 Aug 2005   AET

One of 7 juveniles ringed in 2005 on the Eden Estuary (Fife) in a study to track movements of juvenile birds. Resighted after 37 days at a distance of 67 km WSW from the ringing site.

WHOOPER SWAN

Yellow leg VP3   3 Feb Gogar, Menstrie   Kringluvatn, ICELAND

                                                    12 Aug 2002   NB

First sighting.

Yellow neck 3J01   26 Mar L. Iubhair   ICELAND

                                                    10 Aug 1994   NB

This bird has been seen in Highlands, Angus, Perthshire, Stirlingshire (see 2004 report for further details). Also at R. Suck, IRELAND 5 Jan 2002; L. Tay 11 Jan 2003; Persie Lake, Glenshee 25 Jan 2003; Lonsfjordur, ICELAND 7 Oct 2003; L. Dochart 29 Jan 2004; Monk Myre and Rosemount, Perthshire 12 Nov 2004.

MUTE SWAN

Metal X4860   19 Feb Callander   Castle Semple Loch

                                    Lochwinnoch (Clyde)

                                    15 Dec 2001   CH

Metal X4832   2 Oct High Bonnybridge   Broadwood Loch,

                                    Cumbernauld

                                    22 Sep 2001   CH

Green AUC   20 Aug Forth and Clyde Canal,   unknown
                                                      unknown   CH
                 Bankside, Falkirk
Seen with mate Orange CNV and 6 cygnets there.

Green BUA   16 Jan-7 Mar The Boll, Alva   Bara Loch, nr. Gifford
                                                      (East Lothian)
Skinflats 26 Jan 2003.   16 Aug 1997 AET, ALB

Green HJL   12 Dec Aithrey Loch, Stirling   Dundas Loch (Fife)
                                                      11 Aug 1996   AH
Has been at Airthrey in 1999, 2000, 2003, 2004 and 2005. Further details in the 2004 report.

Green HLY   14 Feb-16 Mar The Boll, Alva   Blackford Pond, Edinburgh
                                                      24 Aug 2003   NB
A well travelled bird. Remained at Blackford Pond until Mar 2004, then moulted at
Musselburgh. Seen Cramond, Edinburgh Sep before making its way to Torry Bay Nov
and Alva in December 2004.

Green HPI   16 Jan, 7 Mar 2006 The Boll, Alva   North Esk Res., Carlops
                                                      30 Aug 2003   AET, ALB
Seen Gartmorn Dam 22 Aug 2004 and The Boll 27 and 29 Dec 2004. From there it went to
Rutherford, E Maxton (Roxburghshire) 14 Oct 2005 before returning to Alva. Further
details in 2004 report.

Green IPT   15-16 Mar The Boll, Alva   Stenton Pond, Glenrothes
                                                      21 Aug 2004   NB, AET
Was originally Green IFN. Was re-ringed at Stenton Pond 1 Jan 2005 and last reported
from there 7 Feb 2005.

Green IPZ   9 Nov, 2 and 12 Dec Airthrey, Stirling Clatto Res., Dundee
                                                      23 Jan 2005   AET
                 16 Jan and 7 Mar 2006 The Boll, Alva

Green ITI   11 Jun High Bonnybridge   High Bonnybridge (Falkirk)
                                                      6 Oct 2002   ALB
Was originally Orange 3BIB; was re-ringed Duddingston Loch, Edinburgh

Orange 3BJC   24 Dec Gartmorn Dam   Gartmorn Dam
                                                      2 Nov 2002   AET
A regular at Gartmorn Dam where present on several dates in 2003 and 2004 (cf. 2004
report). In 2005 recorded with unringed F 19 Mar and with 6 cygnets 20 Jul.

Orange 3BYA   15 Mar The Boll, Alva   Culcreuch Castle, Fintry
                                                      11 Oct 2003   NB
This is the first re-sighting since that date.

Orange 3CAV   2 Oct High Bonnybridge   Broadwood Loch,
                                                      Cumbernauld
                                                      17 Jan 2004   CH
Original ring Orange 3BLV had been lost and was therefore re-ringed.

Orange 3CCY   20 Aug Callendar Park, Falkirk   Callendar Park, Falkirk
                                                      28 Aug 2004   CH
Paired with CCZ. Seen with 6 cygnets.

Orange 3CCZ   20 Aug Callendar Park, Falkirk   Callendar Park, Falkirk
                                                      28 Aug 2004   CH
Paired with CCY. Seen with 6 cygnets.

Orange 3CDA   26 May Stenhousemuir   Stenhousemuir
                                                      28 Oct 2004   CH
Seen with unringed male and 7 cygnets.

Orange 3CHV	2 Oct High Bonnybridge	Colzium, Kilsyth (N. Lanarkshire) 18 Sep 2004	CH
Orange 3CJU	2 Oct High Bonnybridge	Auchenharvie Golf Course Saltcoats (North Ayrshire) 19 Sep 2004	CH
Orange 3CLV	5 Dec Little Denny Res.	Broadwood Loch, Cumbernauld 19 Mar 2005	CH

Also seen at Broadwood Loch 15 May and 20 Aug 2005.

| Orange 3CNV | 20 Aug Forth and Clyde Canal, Bankside, Falkirk | Forth and Clyde Canal, Bankside, Falkirk 20 Aug 2005 | CH |

Original ring Green HFN replaced. Seen with mate Green AUC and 6 cygnets.

| Red UXF | 9 Nov and 2 Dec Airthrey Loch, Stirling | Middleton, Wooler (Northumberland) 4 Aug 2004 | ALB |
| White HFF | 27 Oct South Alloa | Town Loch, Dunfermline 28 Nov 1991 | ALB |

Following the rediscovery of this bird at South Alloa last year after a 10 year absence, the bird was found with a broken leg and was destroyed by the SSPCA. Further details of movements can be found in the 2004 bird report.

| White 284 | 17 Feb The Boll, Alva | Yetholm Loch 24 Aug 2002 | ALB |

CURLEW
L leg: yellow or white - R leg: yellow or white

| | 12 Feb Kinneil lagoon | Staphorst, Overijssel (NETHERLANDS) 1994 or 1995 | AET |

Ringed as a chick as part of a research programme to establish the dispersion patterns of Dutch-ringed Curlews. So far the birds have shown strong site-fidelity, apart from one bird found breeding in north Denmark. The above is the first bird observed in Scotland.

BARN OWL

| GN81079 | 25 Feb M9 Motorway, Stirling | Auchingyle, Balmaha 30 Jun 2004 | TRG |

Juvenile found dead after 240 days at a distance of 35 km E from ringing site.

| GN81084 | 1 Jan Port of Menteith | Flanders Moss 7 Jul 2004 | TRG |

Juvenile female found dead after 178 days at a distance of 5 km WNW from ringing site.

WOODPIGEON

| FP62560 | Alva 23 Jul | Loaningbank, Menstrie 25 Mar 2005 | TRG |

Found dead after 120 days at a distance of 4 km ESE from ringing site.

WAXWING

| White above red above yellow | 17 and 18 Jan Argaty, Braes of Doune | Kelland, Inverurie 31 Oct 2004 | LB, DOE |

Seen 8 times around Aberdeen between 10 Nov and 6 Dec 2004. Thereafter Aboyne (Aberdeenshire) 28 Jan 2005.

BLACKBIRD
CL97805   25 Mar Loaningbank, Menstrie   Carnock, Dunfermline
                                                                   23 Jul 2005   TRG
Female recaptured after 1 year and 148 days at a distance of 21 km from ringing site.

PIED FLYCATCHER
R085611   19 Jun Lendrick, Brig o' Turk   Kenmore Wood, Tarbet
                                                                   9 Jun 2004   TRG
F recaptured after a year and 10 days at a distance of 23 km from the ringing site.

CHAFFINCH
R715222   20 Apr Sheriffmuir   Dunblane
                                                                   24 Aug 2003   AL
1st year male recovered dead after having hit a window after a year and 240 days at a
distance of 4 km from the ringing site.

GREENFINCH
TE18307   25 Mar Loaningbank, Menstrie   Wick (Highland)
                                                                   17 Dec 2004   TRG
F recaptured after 98 days at a distance of 258 km S from the ringing site.

VT29853   9 Feb Montrose (Angus)   Dunblane
                                                                   3 Nov 2002   AL
Male taken by cat after 2 years and 99 days at a distance of 109 km from the ringing
site.

VT29868   7 Aug Linlithgow (West Lothian)   Dunblane
                                                                   30 Nov 2002   AL
Female taken by cat after 2 years and 251 days at a distance of 32 km from the ringing
site.

SISKIN
4483609   20 Jun Strathyre   FRANCE   DJC
Female killed by cat. Details of origin not yet known.

SYSTEMATIC LIST

Codes - S, F and C indicate records from Stirling, Falkirk and Clackmannanshire
"Districts".

* RED-THROATED DIVER *Gavia stellata* (b, w)
F   Five Kinneil 22 Jan; 3 there on 6 Mar and 29 Oct; 2 on 1 Nov; 4 on 5 Nov; 1 on
           12 Nov and 8 on 4 Dec (DT).
S   Pr. at Trossachs loch were calling with some display 24 Jul (MVB). 1 Killin 23 Aug
           (DH).
* BLACK-THROATED DIVER *Gavia arctica* (b, w)
S   Trossachs: AoT at 1st site from 15 Mar to 12 Aug, nesting site not found (Canada
           Geese using usual site), unconfirmed report that they failed on another loch
           close by (DJC, SA). Single bird at 2nd site 25 Apr (RR)
LITTLE GREBE *Tachybaptus ruficollis* (B, w)
           WeBS[1]: 36 inland in Mar and 47 inland in Dec were the max counts for the early
           and late winter periods, both were above the 11-year mean. 72 % were found

[1] For inland WeBS data note that only half the sites were counted in Feb and only ¾ of the
sites were counted in Sep and Oct. Gartmorn Dam was not counted in Feb and Mar.

on still water sites. Recorded from many sites in low numbers, mainly outwith the breeding season.

Monthly maxima at selected sites								
	Dist.	Jan	Feb	Mar	Sep	Oct	Nov	Dec
Little Denny Res.	F	6	0	3	0	0	2	3
R. Devon (Alva - Menstrie)	C	-	-	-	0	6	6	6
Lochs Voil / Doine	S	5	-	2	-	-	8	8
Cambusmore GP	S	4	-	1	17	4	1	4
Lochs Dochart / Iubhair	S	0	8	1	-	-	9	6
L. Lubnaig	S	1	-	10	-	-	3	-
Inland Totals		**28**	**15**	**36**	**27**	**19**	**46**	**47**

F   Breeding: pr. Darnrigg Moss with chicks in May (TF). Site max: 6 Little Denny Res. 21 Jan; 4 Larbert House Loch 11 Mar (NB, MA).

C   Six R. Devon, Alva-Menstrie 31 Oct. Single Maggie's Wood Flood, Fishcross 22 Aug (TC, AET).

S   Breeding: pr. on David Marshall Lodge Pond, Aberfoyle with 4 chicks ca. 1 week old 3 Jun; fully grown juv. Ochlochy Pond, Dunblane 8 Sep. (MVB, NB). Singles Flanders Moss 20 May; Cambusmore/Gart GP 11 Jul (DWP, DT). Site max: 6 Carron Valley Res. 6 Sep; 4 R. Forth, Ladylands - Br. of Frew 13 Dec; 4 R. Teith, Callander 18 Dec (NT, PAL, NB).

GREAT CRESTED GREBE *Podiceps cristatus* (b,W)
    WeBS max: 16 Forth Est. in Nov; 42 inland in Sep is a new high.

Monthly maxima at selected sites													
	Dist	Jan	Feb	Mar	Apr	May	Jun	Jul	Aug	Sep	Oct	Nov	Dec
Kinneil, Forth Est.	F	13	-	10	-	1	-	5	11	14	13	23	-
Gartmorn Dam	C	4	3	-	3	-	3	-	5	13	10	3	2
Carron Valley Res	S	0	1	8	3	-	2	-	-	4	2	0	0
Lake of Menteith	S	3	2	13	9	-	-	-	-	21	-	17	12
Inland Totals		**7**	**2**	**25**	**-**	**-**	**-**	**-**	**-**	**42**	**12**	**23**	**15**
Forth Est. Totals		**2**	**4**	**3**	**-**	**-**	**-**	**-**	**-**	**15**	**1**	**16**	**0**

F   Forth Est: 20 Blackness 13 Feb and 30 there 18 Sep; 23 Kinneil 12 Nov (AB, DT). 2 Black Loch, Limerigg 7 Mar and 1 Nov; 1 there 5 Dec; 1 L. Ellrig 3 Feb and 7 Mar; 1 Skinflats Pools was a rare record 28 Apr (NB, JN, GO).

S   Breeding: Lake of Menteith: 1 bird in almost full breeding plumage 24 Jan; 13 there 19 Mar, 21 birds on 6 Sep included prs. with 2, 2 and 1 juvs., respectively. Juv. Cambusmore GP: 2 ads. on lower pool and 1 on upper pool 2 Apr; pr. on nest lower middle pool (flooded out 28 May) with single bird on upper middle pool 1 May; pr. building nest 3 Jun; pr. lower middle pool with juv. with another pr. collecting weed for nest 12 Jun; 2 prs. on nests - upper middle and lower middle, no sign of earlier juv 11 Jul; still sitting 29 Jul; 2 prs. with broods of 3 and 1 on 16 Aug still there 6 Sep when brood of 3 and single juv. Pr. with 2 juvs. Carron Valley Res. 20 Sep (NB, DT, DAC).
    Other records: 2 W end L. Venachar 22 Jan; 1 there 15 Feb, 15 Mar and 24 Nov (DAC, SA).

*RED-NECKED GREBE *Podiceps grisegena*
F   One Kinneil 16 Sep and 16 Oct (JC). These are the 10th and 11th records, respectively, for the recording area (three on the West Lothian/Forth boundary.

*SLAVONIAN GREBE *Podiceps auritus*
S   One L. Coulter 5 Dec (NB).

* FULMAR *Fulmarus glacialis* (p)
F   Singles Skinflats 9 Sep; Blackness 18 Sep and Kinneil 27 Sep, 1 Oct, 29 Oct and 1 Nov (GO, AB and DT).
*GANNET *Morus bassanus* (p)
F   Imm. W Skinflats 26 Sep with 7 imms. there 30 Sep; 2 juvs. Skinflats flew up the Forth to Kincardine Br. then W inland 28 Oct; 21 juvs. Kinneil 27 Sep with 32 there 1 Oct; 3 on 8 Oct; 1 ad. and 2 juvs. 16 Oct; 1 juv. 29 Oct with 2 juvs. 12 Nov the latest record. 1 juv. W South Alloa 29 Oct (GO, DT, AB, RHD).
S   One juv. W low over Flanders Moss 28 Sep (DWP).
CORMORANT *Phalacrocorax carbo* (S, W)
    Inland: 74 % found on still waters.

WeBS counts at selected sites								
	Dist	Jan	Feb	Mar	Sep	Oct	Nov	Dec
Cambus - Alloa	C/F/S	19	62	-	94	109	124	78
Alloa - Kincardine Br.	C/F	1	86	7	36	18	6	13
Skinflats	F	57	13	23	0	38	28	16
Forth Est. Totals		**87**	**176**	**33**	**159**	**197**	**176**	**119**
R. Forth: Stirling Br. - Fallin	F	5	5	15	15	10	2	4
Lake of Menteith	S	24	-	29	30	-	33	25
Carron Valley Res.	S	4	14	1	12	11	11	6
North Third Res.	S	11	11	3	0	-	8	6
Inland Totals		**89**	**54**	**78**	**72**	**39**	**86**	**97**

F   Other sites: 5 Little Denny Res. 7 Mar (NB).
C   Juv. Delph Pond, Tullibody 15 Mar was unusual; 12 Gartmorn Dam 16 Jan (NB, AET).
S   Twenty at Laggan roost, L. Lubnaig 5 Nov; 6 L. Laggan, Kippen 12 Feb (DJC, DAC).
GREY HERON *Ardea cinerea* (B,W)
    Winter WeBS records widespread throughout the area with 53 % from linear water sites. BBS[1]: recorded at 0.23 b/lkm, over twice the annual mean.

WeBS totals						
Jan	Feb	Mar	Sep	Oct	Nov	Dec
Forth Estuary	15	15	9	52	46	43	47
Inland	67	55	68	71	60	100	90

F   Breeding: At least 28 nests with 57 discarded eggshells Dunmore Wood heronry 24 Apr (AB).
    Site max: 28 Skinflats 18 Sep; 8 Kinneil 5 Sep; 10 R. Forth, Dunmore 10 Jun; 6 Bonnybridge 23 Jan; 8 Little Denny Res. 1 Nov (MVB, DT, RD, MA, NB).
C   Site max: R. Forth: 25 S. Alloa - Kincardine Br. 3 Dec; 24 Cambus - S. Alloa 15 Oct; 7 Alloa Inch 9 Jan (DM, AET). Inland: 21 R. Devon, Dollar - Cambus Weir Nov; 6 Alva Floods 17 Dec (DE, GEL, TC, KW).
    Breeding: Sheardale Braes heronry: 12 nests observed but only 2 apparently occupied 15 Mar (RLG).
S   Breeding: Nyadd heronry – ca. 15 nests from droppings and egg shells. 2 dead

---

[1] Data from 1994 to 1996 are excluded from the long-term mean due to the small sample size of squares surveyed. The mean therefore refers to the period 1997 to 2006. Absolute numbers for several species are small, which should be borne in mind when interpreting the data.

nestlings on ground appeared to be 7-10 days from fledging. Some young may have fledged 26 Apr; 11 Lake of Menteith incl. 7 birds in tops of pines at heronry 19 Mar (JW, NB). Site max: 6 Killin Marshes 10 Jan; 5 R. Teith, Wester Row - Forth conf. 23 Jan; 6 Coustry Pond, Blairdrummond 27 Jan; 5 R. Forth, Cardross Br. - Ladylands 15 Feb; 8 Carron Valley Res. 13 Mar; 20 Nyadd 14 Apr (NB, RHD, AEW, DAC, DWP). 8 Allan Water, district boundary - Dunblane Sep; 6 Cambusmore GP 6 Sep; 5 R. Forth, Stirling Br. - Upper Taylorton 8 Oct; 5 Netherton Marshes 20 Nov (AW, NB, PM, DT).

MUTE SWAN *Cygnus olor* (B,W)
WeBS: 69 % found on still water sites.

Monthly maxima at selected sites and WeBS totals								
	Dist	Jan	Feb	Mar	Sep	Oct	Nov	Dec
Forth/Clyde Canal	F	25	28	12	17	16	21	22
Gartmorn Dam	C	18	14	22	19	17	17	11
R. Devon (Dollar-Cambus)	C	2	7	4	7	23	2	7
Lake of Menteith	S	17	10	16	20	-	19	26
Airthrey Loch	S	15	-	17	19	39	39	35
L. Watston	S	24	35	30	6	4	0	0
R. Forth (Br of Frew - Fallin)	S	17	11	11	3	13	22	14
Inland WeBS totals		**188**	**139**	**152**	**135**	**167**	**192**	**187**

F Breeding: pr. Larbert House Loch hatched 5 cygnets; 2 ads. and 2 juvs. 17 Sep; 2 dead juvs. and no ads. 15 Oct. Pr. displaying Skinflats Pools 5 Apr (MA, AB).

C Breeding: pr. Cambus Village Pool hatched 4 cygnets late Jun still 4 there 20 Aug; pr. Cambus Pools reared 4 juvs. 20 Aug. Bird on nest Longcarse, Rhind 24 Apr (NB, AET, ACR). Site max: 21 Devonmouth Pool (8 juvs.) 3 Feb; 13 Boll Farm, Alva 15 Mar; 23 Gartmorn Dam 12 Apr; 17 Blackdevonmouth Marshes 4 Dec (NB, PMA, RG).

S Breeding: pr. building nest L. Doine 10 Mar; pr. performing courtship display Vale of Coustry, Blairdrummond 27 Jan were with 6 juvs. there 6 Sep; pr. Airthrey Loch hatched and fledged 1 cygnet; pr. Doune Ponds with 6 almost fully grown juvs. 6 Sep. No breeding Gart despite up to 3 pairs being present throughout the summer. Pr with 4 juv. R. Dochart, Killin 1 Sep (NB, MVB, DT, PWS).
Site max: 11 R. Forth, Stirling Br. - Upper Taylorton 18 Dec (PM); 1 juv. found dead under wires on Carse of Lecropt 30 Apr (RHD).

WHOOPER SWAN *Cygnus cygnus* (W)
Inland WeBS peaks: 50 Feb and 56 Dec. 22 % juvs. in 1st winter period (n=265), only 10 % in 2nd (n=143).

F Winter/spring: 10 Kersebrock Farm, N of Larbert 5 Feb; single birds at Kinneil 2 Feb and S. Alloa 4 Apr (AS, RHD) Second winter period: 16 Bowtrees Roundabout, Airth 29 Oct; 5W S. Alloa 29 Oct; 3 Skinflats Pools 2 to 4 Nov; 16 to 26 birds Lochlands Loan, Camelon Nov to Dec (DT, RHD, GO, AB, MA, RD).

C Winter/spring: Devonmouth Pool: 6 on 4 Jan, 24 on 22 Jan; 32 on 12 Feb; 3 Blackgrange, Cambus 15 Jan; 5 R. Devon, A907 - Cambus Weir 14 Feb (NB, AET, DJ, RHD, KW).
2nd winter period: 11 Forest Mill 27 Oct; 4 Alloa Inch roost 5 Nov; 1 R. Devon, Dollar - Tillicoultry 30 Nov (AET, DE).

S Winter/spring: 13 S. Flanders Fm. 4 Jan; 11 Blair Mains, Throsk 10 Jan with 19 there 11 Feb; 3 L. Katrine 31 Jan; 24 South Mid Frew, Thornhill Carse 2 Feb with 30 there 4 Feb and 11 on 10 Feb; 18 L. Dochart 31 Jan with 14 there 7 Feb and 6 on 13 Apr; 19 Burnhead, Cowie 27 Feb; 11 L. Voil 10 Mar; 8 Lake of Menteith 19 Mar with 12 there 22 Mar; 15 L. Iubhair 26 Mar (ad. with yellow neck collar 3J01 back); 3 Thornhill Carse 1 Apr; 4N over Stirling 3 Apr (DAC, RS, SA, DK, NB, RHD, JT, ACR).

Autumn/winter: 21 Blackdub Fm. 13 Oct (the 1st autumn return) with 10 there 29 Nov; 10 R. Forth, Meiklewood 14 Oct; 21 R. Forth, Br. of Frew - E. Frew 25 Oct with 13 there 16 Dec; 17 R. Forth, Ladylands - Br. of Frew 26 Oct; 10 Doune 29 Oct; 7 L. Lubnaig 11 and 19 Dec; 17 R. Forth, E. Frew - Gargunnock Br. 18 Dec; 11 R. Fillan, Crianlarich 23 Dec (DJC, JK, PAL, DOE, NB, ACR).

The 5 yearly International Whooper Swan Census took place during the weekend of 15/16 Jan. The results, along with those of the previous two surveys, are depicted in the table below.

Site	Grid ref	Dist	1995	2000	2005
St Helen's Loch	NS 833796	F	0	0	0
Lochland's Loan	NS 853814	F	0	0	15
Gartmorn Dam	NS 920942	C	6	0	0
Cambus Village Pools	NS 854935	C	0	0	10
Gogar / Blairlogie	NS 838960	S	2	17	10
R. Forth: Stirling Br. – Upper Taylorton	NS 802935	S	0	0	6
Carse of Stirling		S	31	48	0
L. Lubnaig	NN 583131	S	3	14	0
Balquhidder area	NN 535207	S	2	3	6
Lochs Dochart / Iubhair	NN 424268	S	25	10	0
Trossach Lochs		S	0	4	0
Totals			**71**	**96**	**49**
% of juvs.			22	14	20

*BEAN GOOSE *Anser fabalis* (W)

F Max count 265 Slamannan 18 Nov was 3 more than 2004 (BGAG). Slamannan plateau; 164 at roost 11 Feb (speculation that ca.100 birds left at the end of Jan., this would be unusual); last record of 7 on 15 Feb. 11 on 24 Sep were the 1st autumn birds with 105 there 6 Oct and 150 on 13 Nov. Of 125 birds aged in Nov, 14 % were juvs. (BGAG).

PINK-FOOTED GOOSE *Anser brachyrhynchus* (W)

Last spring record: 210 Alloa Inch 2 May. First autumn return: heard over Dunblane 9 Sep (RHD, MVB).

National Autumn Goose Counts				
	Dist	8/9 Oct	4/5 Nov	3/4 Dec
Skinflats (fields)	F	3980	1650	820
Alloa Inch	C	NC	0	670
Gartmorn Dam	C	NC	NC	0
L. Mahaick	S	1060	1200	NC
Cambusmore/Gart GP	S	NC	NC	0
Carse of Stirling (Kippen)	S	NC	NC	1100
Lake of Menteith	S	NC	NC	NC
Totals		**5040**	**2850**	**2590**

F Winter/spring: 900 Slamannan plateau 1 Jan; 1220 Airth 5 Feb with 2150 there 27 Feb and 1820 on 13 Mar. 1000+ Skinflats 28 Feb with 200 there 5 Apr (BGAG, RHD, MVB, GO, AB). Autumn/winter: 250 flying SE Kinneil 29 Oct; 111 flying SW Skinflats 25 Sep with 2740 there 16 Oct; 1040 Airth 16 Oct with 1150 on

5 Nov (DT, RS, MVB).

C   Winter/spring: 383 Alloa Inch 6 Feb with 567 (probably several hundred more hidden) 24 Apr and 210 there 2 May; 1459 Haugh of Blackgrange 22 Jan; 800 Cambus Pools 5 Apr (AET, RHD, ACR). Autumn/winter: 300 flying NE over Tullibody in small skeins 15 Sep (DAC)

S   Winter/spring: 1000 Carse of Lecropt 8 Jan with ca.1400 there 13 Jan; 558 Arnprior 15 Jan; ca. 800 Netherton, Thornhill Carse 20 Jan; 700 West Culmore, Thornhill Carse 30 Jan with 860 there 10 Feb; 300+ Hillhead Farm, Cowie 11 Feb; 1100 Dykes, Fallin 14 Feb; ca. 2300 Netherton, Thornhill Carse 24 Mar; 1500 at Tipperdarroch, Arnprior 19 Mar had a leucistic bird amongst them as did 400 by Flanders Moss 30 Mar. 1000 S of Myme Farm, Flanders Moss 18 Mar whilst 4-5000 flew over the Moss at dusk heading W 21 Mar with 1500 around the edges of the Moss 1 Apr; 1000 Wester Frew, Thornhill Carse on 18 Mar and 15 Apr; 1500 Ashfield N 8 Apr (DT, DJC, NB, CJM, DAC, RS, DWP, DK). Single summering birds were noted at Gart and Glen Finglas, both 3 Jun, the latter was damaged and with Canada Geese (DT, MVB).
Autumn/winter: 12 Fallin SE 11 Sep; 940 SW Argaty in 4 flocks 5 Oct; 500 Doune 29 Oct; 549 Shaw of Touch, Drip Moss 13 Nov; 500 Plean Tower and ca. 500 R. Forth, Drip Moss both 4 Dec; 1350 Kippen/Thornhill area 17 Dec (RHD, MVB, DOE, NB, RAC, DT).

WHITE-FRONTED GOOSE *Anser albifrons* (w)

S   Bird of the Greenland race in flock of 146 Greylag Geese Vale of Coustry, Blairdrummond 24 Nov (NB).

GREYLAG GOOSE *Anser anser* (b, W)
Icelandic birds: last spring record was on the 10 Apr. Date of autumn return confused by the presence of resident birds.

National Autumn Goose Counts				
	Dist	8/9 Oct	4/5 Nov	3/4 Dec
Skinflats (fields)	F	0	0	0
Alloa Inch	C	NC	192	103
Gartmorn Dam	C	NC	NC	180
L. Mahaick	S	0	0	NC
Cambusmore/Gart GP	S	NC	NC	0
Carse of Stirling (Kippen)	S	NC	NC	103
Lake of Menteith	S	NC	NC	NC
Totals		**0**	**192**	**386**

F   Winter/spring: 158 St Helen's Loch, Bonnybridge; 148 Black Loch, Limerigg 7 Jan; 200 Airth 27 Feb. (NB, RHD). Summering birds (probably feral)· 2 Skinflats 2 Aug; 70 Blackness with 9 Canada Geese 28 Aug. (GO, AB). No records of flocks during autumn/winter period.

C   Winter/spring: flock between Alva and R. Devon during Jan peaked at 619 on 9 Jan with 427 there on 16 Jan and 220 on 12 Mar; 535 Haugh of Blackgrange 22 Jan; 258 Midtown, Blackgrange 12 Feb; 490 Gartmorn Dam 20 Feb; 100 Cambus Pools 10 Apr (AET, GEL, MVB, PMA). Summering birds (probably feral): 7 Cambus Pools 3 Jun with 25 there 4 Sep; 2 Tullibody Inch 17 Jul; pr Gartmorn Dam throughout the year (as in 2003 and 2004) (ACR, PMA, AET). Autumn/winter: dusk flight of 55+ into Tullibody Inch 6 Sep; 228 Alloa Inch 18 Sep; 354 Tullibody Inch 15 Oct; 227 Cambus - Alloa Inch 5 Nov with 300 there 17 Nov; 200 R. Devon near Menstrie 23 Dec (MVB, AET, DAC).

S   Winter/spring: 320 R. Forth, Drip Moss 16 Jan; 117 North Third Res. 16 Jan with 405 there 13 Mar; 220 South Mid Frew 10 Feb with 310 there 18 Mar; 201 Blair

Mains, Throsk 11 Feb; 100 Ashfield 22 Feb; 308 East Gogar 15 Mar; 150 S of Myme Farm 18 Mar; 115 Glen Dochart 7 Feb (RAC, BO, DAC, DK, DWP, RS, NB). Summering birds (probably feral): 14 Carron Valley Res. 30 Apr with 27, incl several goslings, there 24 Jun and 15 on 6 Sep; 15 Cambusmore/Gart GP 3 Jun with 18 there 6 Sep; 3 Lake of Menteith 11 May (RG, DT, NT, NB, RAB). Autumn/winter: 150 Flanders Moss 24 Oct; 170 R. Forth, Thornhill Carse 7 Dec; 520 North Third Res. 19 Nov with ca. 250 on 28 Dec; 104 L. Watston 12 Nov; 146 Vale of Coustry, Blairdrummond 24 Nov; 100 Glen Lochay 23 Nov and 114 Killin 23 Dec (DWP, PAL, BO, DOE, NB, PWS).

CANADA GOOSE *Branta canadensis* (b W)

Still expanding in numbers and range, becoming more regular in Clackmannanshire, mostly along the R. Forth.

Site maxima											
	Jan	Feb	Mar	Apr	May	Jun	Aug	Sep	Oct	Nov	Dec
Cambus/Tullibody Inch	0	0	0	-	-	-	216	11	0	1	0
L. Ard	102	119	-	-	-	37	-	9	13	37	11
L. Venachar	36	-	45	-	-	-	-	17	161	133	72
Glen Finglas	-	4	-	-	-	230	-	-	-	-	6
Lake of Menteith	5	-	37	6	-	42	-	27	-	71	20
Cambusmore/Gart GP	162	95	0	27	8	30	316	4	0	99	28
Vale of Coustry	1	13	5	-	-	-	-	10	-	1	69
Glen Dochart/Killin	14	4	7	2	-	-	-	-	25	50	0
WeBS Inland Totals	**246**	**2**	**153**	**-**	**-**	**-**	**-**	**279**	**264**	**374**	**210**

F   Other site max.: 85 Kersebrock Farm, Larbert 8 Jan; 1 Black Loch, Limerigg 21 Jan; 21 St Helen's Loch, Bonnybridge 7 Mar and 5 Dec; 2 Skinflats 14 Jul; 12 Kinneil 27 Aug and 9 Blackness 28 Aug; 50 Airth 29 Oct; 6 Larbert House Loch 5 Nov (RHD, NB, GO, DT, AB, JT, MA).

C   Other site max: 10 Gartmorn Dam 7 Mar; 216 Tullibody Inch 20 Aug included 2 aberrantly coloured birds (mixed white/black and white only heads, respectively); 34 Blackdevonmouth Marshes was 5 Nov (PMA, AET, RLG).

S   Breeding: 42 ads. with 3 broods of Y Lake of Menteith 11 May; 37 ads. with 25 Y L. Ard 2 Jun (RAB, DJC).
     Other site max: 32 Dall, L. Tay 10 Jan; 17 Balvag Marshes, Balquhidder 17 Jan; 10 L. Lubnaig 17 Jan; 53 Gartartan Farm, Gartmore 22 Jan; 7 Westleeton, Cowie 14 Feb; 20 L. Katrine 20 Feb; 4 Hillhead Pond, Thornhill 19 Mar; 6 Wester Cambushinnie 31 Mar; 112 L. Rusky 6 Sep; 7 Alton Farm, Fallin 11 Sep; 77 L. Watston 18 Sep; 25 Torrielochan 16 Oct; 28 L. Arklet 19 Oct; 100 Flanders Moss after dusk 24 Oct; 14 L. Coulter 1 Nov (NB, RHD, RS, DAC, DOE, BB, JM, DWP). R. Forth: 2 Teith conf. - Allan Water conf. 12 Mar; 23 Br. of Frew - E. Frew 25 Oct and 14 Cardross Br. - Ladylands 6 Nov (DT, PAL, AEW).

*BARNACLE GOOSE *Branta leucopsis* (w)

F   One Airth 27 Feb (RHD). 5 SW Skinflats 25 Sep were the 1st of a strong autumn passage (RS). Skinflats: 19 flew in from the E on 2 Oct with 60 there 11 Oct; 24 on 16th; 200 on 25th and 14 on 2 Nov. 4 flew in to land on Kinneil lagoon 1 Oct with 2 on the mudflats with Pink-footed Geese 8 Oct; 21 Airth 16 Oct with 4 Dunmore 29th and 70 on 2 Nov, the latter with ca. 300 Pink-footed Geese (MA, MVB, GO, DT, AB, RHD).

C   One with flock of Pink-footed Geese Blackgrange, Cambus 22 Jan and 10 Apr; 2 Tullibody Inch 15 Oct (RHD, AET, MVB).

S   Winter/Spring: 2 Carse of Lecropt with ca. 1400 Pink-footed Geese 13 Jan; 5

Netherton and 1 Wester Culmore, Thornhill Carse 20th and 30th Jan, both with large Pink-footed Goose flocks; 1 Hillhead Farm, Cowie 11 Feb (DJC, CJM, RS). Autumn passage/winter: 45 Meiklewood, Blairdrummond Carse 14 Oct; 3 R. Forth, Cardross Br.- Ladylands 19 Oct; 1 R. Forth near Kippen 25 Oct; 8 with Pink-footed Geese Whirrieston, Thornhill 31 Oct and 1 with a Pink-footed x Barnacle Goose hybrid Kippen 17 Dec (JK, AEW, PAL, RHD, MVB).

*BRENT GOOSE *Branta bernicla* (w)
One dark-bellied bird Kincardine Br. 9 Jan (MVB, MT).

SHELDUCK *Tadorna tadorna* (b, W)

Inner Forth estuary WeBS Counts							
	Jan	Feb	Mar	Sep	Oct	Nov	Dec
Cambus - S. Alloa	15	103	-	82	6	12	20
S. Alloa - Kincardine Br.	0	34	22	21	0	2	4
Kennetpans	0	9	13	30	4	0	12
Skinflats	108	117	94	630	210	164	214
Grangemouth - Grangepans	214	293	314	824	553	457	191
Grangepans - Carriden	5	8	2	9	21	0	0
Totals	**342**	**564**	**445**	**1596**	**794**	**635**	**441**

F Breeding: 32 S. Alloa included a group of 16 displaying 4 Apr; 3 prs. with br/11, br/5 and br/1 first noted on 25 Jun; max. 95 Skinflats Pools 3 Jun, several juvs. there were with 81 ads. 27 Jun; 6 juvs. R. Forth, Bandeath 12 Aug (RHD, DT, AB, NB). The moult flock at Kinneil peaked at 2905 on 3 Aug down to 935 by 1 Sep; also 488 Skinflats 3 Aug (MVB).

C Regular at Cambus Village and Devonmouth Pools with monthly max. of 50 on 22 Jan; 20 on 13 Feb, 8 on 24 Apr and 17 on 4 May with only the occasional bird thereafter; similar pattern at Cambus Pools with a max of 18 on 21 Mar and 17 on 2nd and 19th Apr (AET, NB, SRS, ACR, RG). Inland: 3 on R. Devon, Alva 3 Apr with 3 on 8 May and 1 on 12 Jun; 2 Maggie's Wood Flood, Fishcross 24 Apr (PMA, AET)

S Breeding: 2 at Hollow Burn, Fallin were displaying and nest prospecting (RHD). There were no inland records.

WIGEON *Anas penelope* (b, W)
Inland WeBS: 74 % found on still water sites.

F Winter/spring site max.: 102 Kinneil 25 Mar; 97 Skinflats Pools 5 Apr (DT, AB). Summering birds: up to 5 Skinflats Pools throughout the summer; 1 R. Forth, Bandeath 3 Jul (GO, AB, AET). Autumn/winter site max.: 57 Blackness 6 Nov; 200 R. Forth, Dunmore 27 Nov; 97 Skinflats Pools 28 Nov; 100 Kinneil Lagoon 11 Dec (AS, AB, GO).

C Winter/spring site max: 59 Kersiepow Pond 4 Jan; 159 on flooded Haugh of Blackgrange 15 Jan; 221 Gartmorn Dam 16 Jan. 1268 Alloa Inches (NB, RHD, AET). Summering birds: 2 Devonmouth Pool 20 May; 4 Tullibody Inch 16 Jul (NB, AET).

S An aberrant M with large white cheek patches at Cambusmore/Gart GP 27 Jan was first seen in Feb 1998 and has been a regular visitor since, also present 10 Mar (NB). Summering birds: 1 Cambusmore/Gart GP 2 Jun (DT). Winter/spring site max.: ca. 135 Blackdub Fm, Drip Moss 13 Jan (DJC). Autumn/winter site max.: 109 R. Forth, Br. of Frew - E. Frew 16 Jan; 152 at L. Dochart; 126 Killin 18 Nov and 23 Dec; 68 North Third Res. 19 Nov (PAL, NB, BO).

WeBS counts at selected sites								
	Dist	Jan	Feb	Mar	Sep	Oct	Nov	Dec
Cambus - Alloa	C/F/S	484	1268	NC	0	37	11	300
Alloa - Kincardine Br.	C/F	1000	20	270	0	200	2	166
Skinflats	F	102	69	58	9	73	78	77
Grangemouth - Grangepans	F	132	103	62	0	25	109	48
Forth Est. Totals		**1718**	**1460**	**390**	**11**	**353**	**200**	**605**
R. Forth: Br of Frew - Teith conf.	S	12	149	53	0	100	282	325
Cambusmore/Gart GP	S	312	325	295	7	84	274	222
L. Dochart, Glen Dochart and Killin	S	236	126	7	NC	NC	160	126
Inland Totals		**949**	**324**	**561**	**15**	**211**	**751**	**753**

*GADWALL   *Anas strepera* (s, w)
F   One Kinneil 5 Sep (DT).
C   Cambus Pools: 4 on 2 Apr with 2 there 10th, 6 (5M and 1 F) on 21st; pr. and 2M
        on 24th; 2 on 12 May (SRS, PMA, AET). Cambus Village Pools: pr. 24 Apr and 2
        May, 2 prs. there 4 May. M Devonmouth Pool 4 May (AET, NB).
S   Male L. Watston 5 Feb; F Polmaise Lagoons, Fallin 27 Oct was a 1st record at this
        newly created wetland feature (DOE, RHD, CW).
TEAL   *Anas crecca*   (b, W)
        Inland WeBS: 52 % found on still water sites.

WeBS counts at selected sites								
	Dist	Jan	Feb	Mar	Sep	Oct	Nov	Dec
Cambus - Alloa	C/F/S	641	380	NC	456	269	193	87
Alloa - Kincardine Br.	C/F	100	91	115	55	23	10	2
Kennetpans	C	168	147	89	9	32	147	73
Skinflats	F	43	189	201	25	102	126	432
Grangemouth - Grangepans	F	35	335	137	156	268	537	220
Forth Est. Totals		**987**	**1142**	**542**	**701**	**747**	**1013**	**814**
R. Carron: Carronbridge - A 905	F	53	48	98	117	37	16	115
Kersiepow Pond, Alva	C	77	26	52	0	NC	33	55
R. Devon: Dollar - Tillicoultry	C	4	38	NC	NC	92	110	60
R. Forth: Stirling Br. - Fallin	S/C	111	133	208	0	155	153	284
L. Mahaick	S	65	NC	9	15	22	92	106
Cambusmore/Gart GP	S	59	NC	27	45	86	63	89
L. Dochart, Glen Dochart and Killin	S	185	37	6	NC	NC	131	63
Inland Totals		**1046**	**598**	**915**	**258**	**601**	**933**	**1234**

F   Winter/spring site max.: 552 Kinneil 13 Jan; 110 Skinflats 3 Apr; 103 S. Alloa 4
        Apr (MVB, GO, RHD). Autumn/winter site max.: 580 Kinneil 19 Nov; 140
        Avonmouth, Kinneil 11 Dec (DT, AB). Summering birds: pr. S. Alloa 2 May
        (RHD).
C   Winter/spring site max: 47 Craigie Pond, Alloa 30 Jan; 39 Cambus Pools 21 Apr
        included a mating pr. (AET). Summering birds: 2 Cambus Pools, Haugh of
        Blackgrange 2 Jun; max. 8 Cambus Pools 5 Jul (AET, ACR). Autumn/winter site
        max.: 37 Devonmouth Pool 2 Sep; 60 Blackdevonmouth Marshes 16 Oct (NB,
        RG).
S   Winter/spring site max.: 102 Dochart Haughs 10 Jan; 64 L. Laggan, Kippen 15
        Jan; 68 Lake of Menteith 24 Jan; 64 L. Venachar 31 Jan with 80 at the W end 15
        Feb; 44 Hillhead Pond, Thornhill 1 Feb (NB, DAC, SA). Summering: pr Cambus-
        more/Gart GP 17 Jun (DT). Autumn/winter site max.: 68 L. Coulter 5 Dec; 52 R.

Forth, E. Frew - Gargunnock Br. 18 Dec and 192 Stirling Br.- Upper Taylorton (NB, ACR, PM).
Breeding: prs. noted S. Alloa (F); Cambus Pools (C); Doune and Cambusmore/ Gart GP (S) (RHD, AET, ACR, DOE, DT).

MALLARD *Anas platyrhynchos* (B,W)
Inland WeBS: 67 % found on still water sites with 28 % being 'duck pond' birds which rely greatly on food from humans. BBS numbers, at 0.76 b/lkm, was slightly higher than the annual mean.

WeBS counts at selected sites								
	Dist	Jan	Feb	Mar	Sep	Oct	Nov	Dec
Gartmorn Dam	C	203	NC	NC	46	140	99	65
Airthrey Loch	S	340	NC	140	226	206	197	250
Inland Totals		**2946**	**917**	**1223**	**1846**	**1720**	**2650**	**2700**
Forth Est. Totals		**191**	**272**	**92**	**300**	**306**	**296**	**327**

F   Breeding: F with 7 ducklings Skinflats Pools 26 Jul (GO). Site max.: 211 Skinflats 7 Sep (RS).

C   Breeding: F flushed from c/2 Pond Wood, Alloa 29 Apr (NB). Cambus Village Pool: F with 7 Y 2 May, F with 5 juvs. and F with 1 juv. 2 Jun, F with 6 Y 28 Jun, F with 4 juvs. and F with 4 chicks 3 Jul, F with 6 Y 27 Jul (NB, AET). Devonmouth Pool: F with 4 Y 28 Jun, F with 3 Y there 15 Jul, F with 3 Y, F with 1 Y and F with 2 Y 27 Jul (NB). Cambus Pools: F with 4 chicks 2 Jun, F with 4 chicks 3 Jul; broods of 5, 7, 11 and 5 Y on 5 Jul (AET, ACR). F with 7 Y Maggie's Wood Flood, Fishcross 14 Jun and F with 4 chicks there 3 Jul (NB, AET).

S   Breeding: Cambusmore/Gart GP: F with 2 Y Gart Loch 28 May and F with 6 Y on the lower pool in Cambusmore GP 3 Jul (NB). Site max.: 228 Killin Marshes 10 Jan (NB).

PINTAIL *Anas acuta* (W)

Monthly site maxima												
	D	Jan	Feb	Mar	Apr	May	Jun	Jul	Aug	Sep	Oct	Nov	Dec
Skinflats	F	80	72	54	4	-	-	-	-	18	38	47	66
Kinneil	F	4	-	-	-	-	-	-	-	3	22	34	-

F   Max of 45 (23M, 22 F) Skinflat Pools 27 Feb and 27 there 19 Dec (AB).
C   M Cambus Village Pools 2 Jun (AET).

*SHOVELER *Anas clypeata* (p)
F   Two F Kinneil 5 Sep and 4 there 29 Oct; M Skinflats 26 Apr (DT, GO).

POCHARD *Aythya ferina* (W)

WeBS counts at selected sites								
	Dist	Jan	Feb	Mar	Sep	Oct	Nov	Dec
Gartmorn Dam	C	22	NC	NC	16	23	31	6
Lake of Menteith	S	0	NC	O	6	NC	54	60
Inland Totals		**45**	**37**	**7**	**43**	**124**	**154**	**105**

F   Very scarce: 10 Kinneil 27 Sep; 10 R. Carron conf. with the Forth and Clyde Canal is unusual (rarely found on linear water features) 15 Dec; 1 Skinflats Pools Jun to Nov; 1 Callendar Park Loch 13 Feb and 18 Sep (DT, RK, GO, AB, RD, JF).

C   Two Gartmorn Dam 9 Aug; 12 Blackdevonmouth Marshes 5 Nov (PMA, RLG).

S   Site max.: 16 Carron Valley Res. 15 Jan; 77 Gart GP 29 Oct; 24 L. Mahaick 29 Oct; 54 Lake of Menteith 13 Nov with 60 there 12 Dec; 24 L. Venachar 24 Nov; 24 L. Ard 20 Dec (DAC, NB, SA, JM). Over-summering birds: up to 4 Cambusmore/Gart GP May - Aug (NB, DT).

TUFTED DUCK *Aythya fuligula* (B, W)

		Site maxima							
	Dist	Jan	Feb	Mar	Aug	Sep	Oct	Nov	Dec
Gartmorn Dam	C	66	NC	NC	80	34	65	105	53
Cambusmore / Gart GP	S	18	NC	13	39	39	23	31	23
Lake of Menteith	S	56	NC	29	-	0	NC	72	49
Vale of Coustry	S	58	NC	51	-	14	NC	47	42
WeBS Inland Totals		351	109	206	NC	156	141	388	295

Only 6 birds recorded on linear water features.
> Breeding: prs. and summering birds at Skinflat Pools; Doune Lodge, Braes of Doune; Cambusmore/Gart GP; Upper Lanrick Dam, Teith Valley (AB, GO, DOE, PWS, DT).

F   Site max.: 29 Kinneil House Curling Pond 10 Dec; 11 Kinneil 16 Oct (MA, DT).
C   Five on R. Devon, Menstrie 13 Apr to 15 May (DAC). This follows a pattern of sightings on the R. Devon, Alva-Menstrie stretch in April-July every year between 1995 and 2000.
S   Site max.: 30 L. Watston 5 Feb; 20 Airthrey Loch 5 Nov (DOE, MK).

*SCAUP *Aythya marina* (s, w)
F   One R. Carron, Grangemouth 9 Jan. Skinflats Pools: 4M, 1F and 1 imm. 9 Sep; F 25 Oct; 1 on 5 Nov; F/Imm 28 Nov and 2 on 3 Dec. (MVB, GO, AB). Kinneil: 2M on 21 Jun; 7M and 2F on 25 Sep; F 27 Sep; 4 on 1 Oct; 3 on 1 Nov and 2 on 6 Nov (DT, GO, MVB).
S   Two 1st winter F Lake of Menteith 24 Jan; M Doune Lodge, Buchany 24 Mar (NB, DOE).

EIDER *Somateria mollissima* (w, s)
F   Six R. Carron, Grangemouth with 14 there 13 Mar; recorded at Kinneil throughout the year with max. of 12 (9M) 6 Mar; 3F there 18 Jul and pr. 19 Nov being the last. 3M Blackness, Forth Est. 30 Oct with 3F there 11 Nov; 2M R. Forth, Dunmore 14 Jun (MVB, DT, MA, PGC).

LONG-TAILED DUCK *Clangula hyemalis* (w)
> Large number of records this year.

F   Skinflats Pools: F and imm. 25 Oct and 2 Nov; 1 there 5 Nov (AB, GO, MVB). 1 Kinneil Lagoon 6 Nov with F there 13 Nov (MVB, DAC). Imm R. Forth, S. Alloa 27 and 29 Oct (RHD).
C   F Cambus Pools 24 Oct, 4 and 5 Nov (SRS, DAC, RG). Singles Longcarse Farm Pond, Alloa and Maggie's Wood Flood, Fishcross 5 Nov (AET).
S   Lake of Menteith: F overwintered 2004/05; 3F there 24 Jan; F 28 Jan, 5 Feb and 19 Mar; 2 ad. M, 1 imm. M and 1 juv. 13 Nov were the largest group yet recorded in the recording area; pr. there 12 Dec (NB, DAC, DK). Imm Polmaise Lagoons, Fallin 27 Oct and 5 Nov (RHD).

*COMMON SCOTER
F   F/imm. Forth Est. Kinneil 11 and 26 Dec (AB, GO).

GOLDENEYE *Bucephala clangula* (W)
> Inland WeBS: 76 % recorded from still water sites. Sex ratio counts from Jan-Mar showed 21 % M (n= 616), whereas those from Nov to Dec showed only 11 % M (n=323). There continues to be a marked build up of numbers on the lower R. Devon and R. Forth (Cambus-Alloa) during the Jan to Mar period.

F   Site max: 32 Black Loch, Limerigg 7 Mar; ca. 30 Skinflat Pools 18 Mar (NB, AB).
C   Site max: 55 Alloa Inches 6 Feb (AET).
S   Site max: 22 L. Venachar 31 Jan and 15 Mar; 18 L. Katrine 15 Mar; 15 still on L. Dochart 13 Apr (SA, JT). 4 Airthrey Loch 30 Nov were very unusual; 26 R. Forth,

Stirling Br. - Upper Taylorton 18 Dec; 81 R. Forth, East Frew - Gargunnock Br. 18 Dec; 23 R. Lochay, Killin 23 Dec (MVB, PM, ACR, NB). Breeding/oversummering: pr. L.Tay, Killin 16 May and 1 on 2 Jun (PWS).

WebS counts at selected sites								
	Dist	Jan	Feb	Mar	Sep	Oct	Nov	Dec
Gartmorn Dam	C	59	NC	NC	0	5	23	28
R. Devon: Menstrie Br - Cambus	C	45	60	31	0	4	0	22
Carron Valley Res	S	17	31	26	0	0	7	15
Lake of Menteith	S	184	NC	177	NC	NC	171	121
Lochs Dochart / Iubhair	S	14	33	46	NC	NC	63	31
Inland Totals		**432**	**219**	**476**	**2**	**21**	**398**	**473**
Inner Forth Est Totals		**47**	**78**	**21**	**1**	**3**	**12**	**36**

*SMEW *Mergus albellus* (w)
S   Redhead R. Forth, Br. of Frew - E. Frew 7 Dec. This is the 1st record from a non-tidal river (PAL).
RED-BREASTED MERGANSER *Mergus serrator* (B, W)
    Inland WebS: 89 % found on linear water features (peak numbers in Feb/March all on linear features).

WebS counts at selected sites								
	Dist	Jan	Feb	Mar	Sep	Oct	Nov	Dec
Forth Est		43	41	27	4	15	31	49
Inland Totals		6	12	18	0	0	6	3

F   Site max: 32 Kinneil 13 Jan, 14 there 30 Jul and 50 on 29 Oct (MVB, DT). 20 R. Forth, Dunmore 27 Nov; 6 Skinflats Pools 27 Feb; 25 Skinflats 3 Dec (AB, MVB). 2 Forth and Clyde Canal, Camelon - R. Carron 16 Feb; 3 (2M) R. Carron, Carronbridge - Carron House 17 Jan and 14 Mar; (DM, AB, MA). F/imm. Faughlin Res 1 Nov (NB). Breeding: F with 4Y Avonmouth, Kinneil 2 Jun (AB).
C   Pr. Alloa Inches 9 Jan; 1 Cambus Pools 5 Nov (AET, RG).
S   Site max: 9 R. Forth, Teith conf. - Stirling Br. 12 Mar; 5 Craigforth 10 Apr; M Gart Loch 7 May; 2 R. Forth, E Frew - Gargunnock Br. 18 Dec; 3 L. Ard 23 Nov (DT, GF, RHD, ACR, JM).
GOOSANDER *Mergus merganser* (B, W)
    Inland WebS: 70 % found on linear water features. Sex ratio counts from some sites in Nov/Dec showed 39 % M (n=83).

WebS counts at selected sites								
	Dist	Jan	Feb	Mar	Sep	Oct	Nov	Dec
R. Forth: Teith conf. - Stirling Br.	S	35	8	7	0	14	22	12
R. Forth: Stirling Br. - Upper Taylorton	S	1	2	22	0	4	30	44
R. Forth: Cambus - Alloa	C/F	8	5	NC	6	3	27	36
Inland Totals		**89**	**61**	**106**	**20**	**72**	**92**	**132**

F   Breeding: F with 5 juvs. R. Carron, Carronshore 13 Aug (AB). Site max: 6 L. Ellrig 19 Jan; 7 R. Carron, Larbert - Carron Br. 23 Jan; 12 R. Carron, Grangemouth 18 Sep (JN, MA, MVB).
C   Site max: 12 Cambus Pools 5 Apr with 10 there 4 Sep; 12 R. Devon, Cambus 27 Oct; 11 R. Devon, Dollar - Tillicoultry 30 Dec (ACR, PMA, DAC, DE).
S   Breeding: F with 8 small Y Lake of Menteith 11 May; pr. L. Tay, Killin 13 Apr

with 1 there 24 May; 5 L. Ard 6 May; 2 Carron Valley Res 30 May (RAB, PWS, GC, RG).
Winter/spring site max.: 20 (15M) Airthrey Loch 9 Feb; 7 L. Laggan, Kippen 12 Feb; 17 Quarry Loch, Vale of Coustry 17 Feb; 9 R. Forth, West Carse Fm. - Teith conf. 10 Mar; 5 North Third Res. 13 Mar; 14 R. Teith 13 Mar; 4 prs. R. Forth, Craigforth 10 Apr; 7 (4M) Cambusmore/Gart GP 22 Apr (MVB, DAC, RAC, BO, RHD, DT).
Autumn/winter site max.: 6 L. Venachar 21 Sep and 20 Dec; 25 L. Ard 19 Oct; 5 (1M) Glen Finglas Res 7 Nov; 44 R. Forth, Stirling Br. - Upper Taylorton 18 Dec; 10 (8M) Quarry Loch, Vale of Coustry 20 Dec (SA, JM, PM, NB).

RED KITE *Milvus milvus* (b ,W)

Only 3 birds recorded on BBS (annual range 0 - 4 birds).

F   One above the centre of Falkirk 7 Jul is the first record for Falkirk District (MA).

S   Breeding: 21 territories occupied; 17 prs. laying eggs of which 11 were successful, fledging 22 Y. Poor food supply in April contributed to low productivity (DOE).
Other sightings: max. 29 at winter roost Braes of Doune 21 Jan; max. Argaty, Braes of Doune feeding station: 35 in Jan and 25 in Nov. Many sightings from the Braes of Doune, Lanrick, Cromlix and Kinbuck areas. 2 by Callander 27 May; 1 Torrielochan 18 Sep and 6 Dec; 1 Flanders Moss 20 and 23 May (different birds) (ES, BB, DWP). Birds from Central Scotland were recorded at Tomatin, Highland and at Laurieston, Dumfries and Galloway. Please try to note wing tag colours on any bird seen and send along with details (place, date etc) to duncan.orr-ewing@rspb.org.uk .

*MARSH HARRIER *Circus aeruginosus* (p)

S   M Cromlix 26 Mar (DOE).

*HEN HARRIER *Circus cyaneus* (b, w)

10 M and 6 ringtails noted in 2005 - almost identical to 2004.

F   One Newcraig, Slamannan 6 Feb; F Kinneil 21 Feb and 1 there 21 Mar; M Slamannan 4 to 14 Dec; F/imm. Darnrigg Moss 12 Dec (MVB, DT, BTO, BGAG, TF).

S   Flanders Moss: 3 M coming into roost at dusk 16 Jan; M seen several times during Jan, Feb and Mar (DWP, DAC, SRS). L. Mahaick: F/imm. 2 Feb, 2 there 3rd , pr. on 5th and 1 on 14th (SRS, DOE). F/imm. Doune 14 Feb; F Argaty, Braes of Doune 21 Feb; F/imm. Kilmahog 14 Apr; M Cringate Law, Gargunnock Hills 3 Jun; Ringtail Craigforth, Stirling 3 Sep; M Myme Farm, Thornhill Carse 17 Oct (DJC, DOE, AB, ACR, DT).

*GOSHAWK *Accipiter gentilis* (b,w)

S   F Callander 14 Apr was interacting with a Red Kite; 1 Balquhidder 19 Aug (DJC)
Correction: juv. reported in 2004 in Strathyre was a 1st year rufous F Sparrowhawk following study of photographs (DJC).

SPARROWHAWK *Accipiter nisus* (B, W)

Many records throughout the area, mainly Jan to Apr and Sep to Dec. Monthly max. of 4 on inland WeBS counts (Oct and Dec) equals the lowest total in 9 years (annual monthly max. mean: 6, range: 4-9 from 1997 to 2004). Recorded in several gardens chasing prey as diverse as finches, tits, pigeons, Blackbird and House Sparrow but no records of any actual kills. One hit a kitchen window whilst chasing a Blackbird. Only 4 birds recorded on BBS (annual range: 1-6).

F   Records from Dorrator, Gartcows and West Mains Industrial Estate (all Falkirk); Blackness; Bo'ness; Kinneil; Skinflats (all year, no signs of breeding); St Helen's Loch, Bonnybridge; Strathavon Fm, Slamannan and Drumbowie, Denny.

C   Records from R. Devon, Dollar-Menstrie (several); Tullibody; Alva Glen;

Tillicoultry; Woodland Park, Alva; Blackgrange and Gartmorn Dam.
S   Breeding summary: 11 sites checked, 9 occupied with 7 sites rearing a minimum of 20Y (DA, DOE).
Records from East Gogar; Carron Valley Res; R. Forth, Cardross Br-Stirling Br. (several); Netherton Marsh, BoA; Lake of Menteith; L. Watston, Doune; Braes of Doune; Argaty; Cromlix; displaying at Wood of Doune; Dunblane; Strathyre; Lendrick Lodge, L. Venachar; Kingshouse, Balquhidder and Killin.

BUZZARD *Buteo buteo* (B,W)
Now widespread and numerous throughout the area, commonly seen over built-up areas. Most common raptor on inland WeBS counts with monthly max. of 51 in Mar (annual monthly max mean of 42 with range of 28-58 from 1997 to 2004). Recorded on BBS at rate of 0.46 b/lkm, slightly above the mean (annual range: 0.26-0.46 b/lkm).
Breeding: 106 known territories checked in the Doune/Aberfoyle/Strathyre areas and 5 territories in the Ochils. 81 were occupied by ad. prs., 60 laid eggs of which 9 prs. failed with 46 prs. fledging 77Y (DOE, DA, JC).
F   Five Kinneil Gate 14 Feb; 6 Kinneil 25 Jun (AS, DT).
C   Eight R. Devon (Tillicoultry - Alva) 17 Dec (GEL).
S   Eight Lerrocks Fm, Argaty 2 Jan; 8 R. Teith, Wester Row - Forth conf. 20 Feb; 6 Braes of Doune 3 Feb with 10 there 20 Mar; 15 Carse of Lecropt 6 Feb; 6 Glen Dochart 7 Feb; 5 Stockbridge, Dunblane 25 Mar; 8 Kinbuck 13 Apr (MM, RHD, ACR, DT, NB, DJC). 7 Torbrex, Stirling 3 Jun; bird picking at apparently dead F pheasant on Meiklewood House road 25 Jun flew off on approach, at which, the pheasant got up and ran away (DJM, NB). 5 R. Forth, Meiklewood 14 Oct; 11 in field of winter cereal Argaty 5 Nov; 5 in field of rape Glenhead, Dunblane 7 Nov (MVB, NB).

GOLDEN EAGLE *Aquila chrysaetos* (b, w)
S   One Braes of Doune 14 Feb; 1 above Killin 3 May; 2 imms. mobbed by Raven and Buzzard Kirkton Farm, Tyndrum 19 Aug (DOE, RC, DH).

OSPREY *Pandion haliaetus* (B)
First of year Doune 23 Mar is the earliest since recording began in 1990 (mean arrival date of 4 Apr with range of 29 Mar to 22 Apr between 1990 to 2004). Other early arrivals were 1 Lake of Menteith 24 Mar; 1 over Killin 26 Mar carrying nesting material and 1 Cromlix 29 Mar (DOE, DJC, NB). Last: 1 Wharry Burn, Sheriffmuir 5 Nov; 1 N shore L. Venachar 13 Nov are the latest ever recorded, the previous late record being of a bird at L. Drunkie, Trossachs 3 Nov 1990 (SDRS).
F   Daily visitor to Black Loch, Limerigg mid Apr to late Aug; 1 Buckieburn Res 3 Jun (IK, AB).
S   Breeding summary: 14 prs. laid eggs of which 3 failed and 11 prs. fledged 23Y (DOE, DA, RAB). Up to 2 birds Carron Valley Res 8 Apr to 6 Jul; 1 Glenample 7 May; 1 Killin 10 Aug; 1 Keir House W with large fish 18 Aug (DT, MG, PWS, DT, PW).

KESTREL *Falco tinnunculus* (B,W)
The 2nd most common raptor recorded on inland WeBS counts with a monthly high of 14 in Dec (annual monthly max. mean of 17 with range of 13-29 from 1997 to 2004). Six birds were recorded on BBS, the same as the mean (annual range: 3-13 birds).
F   Widespread throughout the year with records from 12 locations in the Grangemouth, Bo'ness and Blackness area (AS). Pr. Skinflats all year but no evidence of breeding. Also records from Junction 5, M80; Junction 7, M9 and S. Alloa (AB, GO, MML, RHD).

S   Breeding: 9 prs. between Cromlix to Drumloist with br/2 ringed at Dalbrack, Braes of Doune 3 Jul; F carrying nesting material Callander 7 Apr; pr. fledged br/3 Stirling Castle (DOE, RMcK). Records of single birds from Carron Valley Res.; Fallin; King's Park, Stirling (regular); Thornhill; Killin and Glen Lochay (RG, RHD, ACR, MO, RC, PWS).

*MERLIN   *Falco columbarius* (b?,w)

F   M Skinflats 24 Feb; 1 Kersebrock Farm, Larbert 29 Oct; 1 Slamannan 6 Nov and 24 Dec, the latter chasing Redwings (RHD, GO, BGAG)

S   One Doune 2 Jan; 1 Flanders Moss 1 Feb; F Carse of Lecropt 10 Mar; (DOE, DWP, MVB). F/imm. mobbed and chased a Red Kite at Argaty, Braes of Doune 25 Oct; M Polmaise Lagoons, Fallin 5 Nov; 1 R. Forth, Br. of Frew - E. Frew 16 Nov (DJC, RHD, PAL).

PEREGRINE   *Falco peregrinus* (B, W)

F   One Kinneil Lagoon 4 Jan; ad. N Carron, Falkirk 25 Jun; M Skinflats 5 Sep with juv. there chasing Carrion Crows along the sea wall 28 Sep; ad. Kinneil 27 Sep; ad. M South Alloa 27 Oct; 1 Larbert House Loch 5 Nov and 1 West Mains Industrial Est, Falkirk 3 Dec (RS, AB, GO, RHD, MA).

C   One W Solsgirth Mine, NE of Forest Mill 13 Jun (NB).

S   Single birds at Argaty, Braes of Doune 23 Jan and 12 Feb with juv. there chasing thrushes 25 Oct (DJC, DK). 1 Fallin 22 Jan; 1 Thornhill Carse 20 Jan and 8 Feb; ad. Keir chasing Woodpigeon 13 Jan; 1 R. Teith, Daldorn to Deanston 6 Feb; 1 Logie 17 Feb; 2 Blairlogie 10 Apr and 1 there 13 Dec (RHD, DJC, DK, DOE, SRS, DAC). Ad. M Kippen 4 Mar; 1 Gart, Callander 16 Apr; 1 Stirling 20 Apr; 1 Kippen 19 and 23 Aug (DJC, DOE, DRO, DH).

*RED GROUSE   *Lagopus lagopus* (B, W)

Generally under-recorded, no records from NW of area. Numbers on BBS were up slightly on 2004 but still only 50 % of the annual mean with a bird encountered every 10 linear km in the mountain and moorland habitat category.

S   Breeding: Single week old chick in Upper Glen Kendrum, Lochearnhead 4 Jul (DJC).

Heard on Beinn nan Eachan, Killin 3 May; 2 The Vine, L. Ard Forest 9 Jun; 5 Touch Res. 26 Oct; 4 Ardnandave Hill, L. Lubnaig 20 Nov (RC, AS, SRS, DJC).

*BLACK GROUSE   *Tetrao tetrix* (B, W)

A total of 33 leks were checked (range: 1 to 20 Ms) with a total of 112 Ms (CSBGCG).

S   Breeding: max 11 (7M) at Carron Valley lek 2 May; single M on L. Voil lek 7 Apr; 4 M Bracklinn, Callander 5 Jun (RG, DOE). 7 L. Arklet 21 Jan; 5 Buckieburn Res. 30 Nov (DJC, CW).

GREY PARTRIDGE   *Perdix perdix* (B, W)

Recorded at very low frequency on BBS with only 2 birds this year, 1 below the mean (annual range: 0 - 8).

F   Breeding: ad. with 12Y Skinflats 29 Jul and ad. with 5Y there 30 Aug (GO). Covey of 7 R. Carron between Falkirk and Stenhousemuir 2 and 23 Jan; pr. Skinflats 11 Mar to 12 May; pr. Blackness 2 Apr; 2 Kinneil 23 Feb (MA, AB, GO, DAC, DT). Covey of 6 Orchardhead, Skinflats 5 Nov; covey of 12 Dorrator Fm., Camelon 6 Nov; covey of 11 Higgins Neuk 3 Dec with 6 there 31 Dec (MVB, MA, AET).

C   R. Devon, Alva - Menstrie: pr. 24 Apr, 15 and 30 May; coveys of 7 on 9 Nov and 10 there 23 Dec (DAC).

S   No records received for the Carse of Stirling. Pr. Burnhead, Cowie 6 Feb; pr. Newpark Fm., Bannockburn 19 Jun; pr. Deanston Fm 25 Jun (RHD, JF, SRS).

QUAIL   Coturnix coturnix
S   Two calling ads. in set-a-side Carse of Lecropt 21 Jul, some quiet piping sounds may have been juvs. Ad. heard there 9 Aug (DT).
PHEASANT   *Phasianus colchicus*   (B, W)
        Very large numbers released on shooting estates, otherwise widespread but in small numbers. Recorded on BBS at the highest frequency to date, 0.71 b/lkm (annual range: 0.27-0.71), 39 % above the 8-year mean with 1.4 b/lkm on farmland and 0.3 b/lkm in conifer woodland and conifer/moorland edge.
F   Up to 3 Skinflats in spring; 20 Kinneil 19 Nov (GO, DT).
S   M with damaged leg came to Dunblane garden to feed on regular basis in May (NB).
WATER RAIL   *Rallus aquaticus*   (b, w)
F   One in pool Stirling Rd., Camelon 30 Jan; 1 West Mains Pond 11 Mar; max. 5 calling Ms Skinflats 23 Mar. Singles Kinneil 21 Apr, 7 Jul and 29 Oct (MA, GO, DT).
C   One calling Cambus Pools 21 and 24 Apr, 12 May; 1 there 18 Aug. 1 Tullibody Inch 16 Jul and 17 Nov; 1 Devonmouth Pool, Cambus 10 Aug; 1 in R. Forth reedbeds, Blackgrange 11 Sep; 1 Gartmorn Dam 19 Nov (AET, SRS, DAC, ACR, RD).
S   One calling Blackwater Marshes, L. Venachar 24 Jul; 1 L. Watston 18 Sep and 23 Oct; 1 L. Ard 20 Dec (MVB, DOE, JM).
MOORHEN   *Gallinula chloropus*   (B,W)
        WeBS: 37 % recorded on linear water features.
F   Numbers on the Union Canal fell yet again, with a monthly max. of 7 (Jan), 11 % of the 1997-2000 mean (mean of annual monthly max.: 65; annual range: 30-101), having fallen each year since restoration work commenced. Numbers on the Forth/Clyde Canal (R. Carron to Bonnybridge) dropped to 54 % of the 1996-2000 mean, (mean of annual monthly max.: 27; annual range: 24-34), during restoration work and with a monthly max. of 18 (Feb) this year are still 33 % down. (The 2001-2005 mean of annual monthly max. = 17 with annual range of 15-19). (NB).
        Site max.: 5 Larbert House Loch 11 Mar and 15 Oct; 25 Callander Park Loch 18 Sep; 7 West Mains Pond, Falkirk 17 Sep; 6 Kinneil House Curling Pond 9 Oct (MA, JF).
C   Breeding: max. 3 ads. and 3 juvs. Cambus Pools 20 Aug; ad. and 1 juv. Cambus Village Pools 20 Aug; ad and 4 juvs. Solsgirth Mine settling ponds 15 Jul; ad. and 2 juvs. Delph Pond, Tullibody 2 Sep (AET, NB).
        Site max.: 8 Inglewood Pond, Alloa 3 Feb; 10 R. Devon, Alva-Menstrie 18 Nov; 10 Gartmorn Dam 4 Dec (NB, TC, GF).
S   Breeding: 2 prs. attempted to breed Airthrey Loch in Apr; 2 ads. and 4 juvs. Doune Ponds 6 Sep; 4 juvs. by the fish cages, Lake of Menteith 6 Sep (MVB, NB). Site max.: 6 Airthrey Loch compared with a monthly max. of 34 in 1995; 5 Doune Ponds 24 Nov; 7 R. Teith, The Meadows, Callander 6 Sep; 9 Vale of Coustry, Blairdrummond 6 Sep; 5 R. Forth, Br of Frew-East Frew (MK, NB, PAL).

COOT *Fulica atra* (B, W)
WeBS: very few on linear water features, monthly max of only 4.

WeBS counts at selected sites								
	Dist	Jan	Feb	Mar	Sep	Oct	Nov	Dec
Gartmorn Dam	C	352	NC	NC	42	108	131	95
Lake of Menteith	S	86	NC	33	26	NC	183	122
Inland Totals		**674**	**85**	**176**	**167**	**195**	**439**	**348**

F   Site max.: 21 Callendar House Loch 13 Nov; 1 Skinflats 8 Aug (JF, GO).

C   Breeding: Cambus Village Pool: ad. ON 9 May and 2 Jun; ads. feeding 2 chicks 28 Jun; 1 juv. with ad. ON 15 Jul; 2 juvs. with no ad. ON 20 Jul (NB, AET). Site max.: 131 Gartmorn Dam Nov was low (GF).

S   Breeding: Airthrey Loch: 2 prs. plus 11 ON 11 Apr; 7 prs. with 3 broods and 2 ON 20 Jun (MVB). Site max: 35 Airthrey 30 Nov; 3 Touch Res. 18 Sep (MVB, ES).

OYSTERCATCHER *Haematopus ostralegus* (B,W)
Numbers on BBS were almost double the low count of 2004 but at 0.73 b/lkm still 20 % down on the mean (annual range: 0.41-1.64 b/lkm). Almost all the records came from farmland habitat. The monthly max. from inland WeBS counts was 723 (Mar), 6 % down on the 9-year mean (annual range: 289-1224). WeBS estuary peaks in each winter were 159 Mar and 152 Sep. Inland WeBS peak 723 (Mar) (annual range: 723-1224; mean: 990).

F   73 Kinneil 6 Feb, 55 Skinflats and 69 Kincardine Br. to Alloa 13 Mar the peak numbers early in the year (MVB, JC, DM). 42 Skinflats Pools 29 May (AB). 90 returned Kinneil 5 Aug with 110 there on 16 Sep and 125 on 19 Nov (DT, JC). 70 Skinflats 10 Aug and 55 there on 3 Dec (AB, MVB, DL). 63 Blackness 6 Nov (AS).

C   31 Rhind, Alloa 6 Feb (AET).

S   Return inland: 4 Craigforth 16 Jan, 6 Ashfield 29 Jan, 2 Airthrey 31 Jan, present Doune on 4 Feb, 13 Gart GP 5 Feb. Peak numbers later were 220 Craigforth and Lecropt 20 Feb, 140 Ashfield 5 Mar, 192 Vale of Coustry 23 Mar (DT, DWP, DOE, MVB, NB). 26 Gart GP 22 Jun was the only post-breeding flock reported (DT).

*AVOCET *Recurvirostra avosetta*
F   One Skinflats Pools 14-17 May (GO, AET, RB, BTO).

*LITTLE RINGED PLOVER *Charadrius dubius*
S   A pair was displaying Gart GP on 2nd Jun with 1 bird also displaying the following day, showing a nest shuffling movement. 2 birds again on 7th. On 17th 1 bird appeared to be on a nest in the same spot as the bird seen on the 3rd. The birds were not seen on 22nd or subsequently (DT). This is only the second breeding record for the recording area.

RINGED PLOVER *Charadrius hiaticula* (b,W)
WEBS estuary peaks in each winter were 54 Jan and 37 Nov.

F   As usual most at Kinneil with much smaller numbers at Bo'ness, Skinflats Pools and at the mouth of the Carron. 54 Kinneil 15 Jan was the largest flock early in the year (JC). 2 Carron, Skinflats 13 Mar; 9 Skinflats Pools 15 May (MVB, GO). 2 Skinflats Pools 3 Aug, 27 Kinneil 16 Sep, 57 there on 8 Oct and 37 on 5 Nov (MVB, JC, DT).

C   Two Solsgirth Mine near Forestmill 30 May (NB).

S   Four Gart 2 Apr and 1 May; a small chick there on 28 May, 3 ads. on 3 Jun, 2 ads. on 11 Jul (NB, DT).

*DOTTEREL *Charadrius morinellus*
S   Two Ben Ledi 28 May (DA).

GOLDEN PLOVER   *Pluvialis apricaria* (B,W)
   WeBS estuary peaks in each winter were 840 Jan and 1400 Nov.
F   The large flock from autumn 2004 remained at Kinneil to mid-Jan with 1070 there on 15th, 200 still there 6 Mar (MVB, DT). 12 Skinflats 3 Aug were the first noted back on the estuary and 19 Kinneil 5 Sep the first there but numbers remained low until the end of Sep. A poor autumn on the estuary, especially at Kinneil where the large flocks of the previous two autumns did not materialise. 800 Kinneil 8 Oct was the peak there, later 260 on 3 Dec. 1400 Kincardine Br. 5 Nov was the only flock over 100 on the Skinflats section of the estuary (MVB, DT, JC).
S   70 South Mid Frew 15 Apr (DJC) was the only flock noted on the Carse. 25 Hill of Row 14 Oct (MVB).

GREY PLOVER   *Pluvialis squatarola* (W)
   A poor year.
F   One Kinneil 19 Feb was the only sighting in the first winter period (MVB). 1 Skinflats 25-26 Jul was early (GO). Later 16 Skinflats 5 Nov and 3 on 3 Dec (MVB).

LAPWING   *Vanellus vanellus* (B,W)
   Numbers on BBS were over twice those of last year's slump at 0.71 b/lkm, although still 11 % down on the mean (annual range: 0.23-1.72 b/lkm). All the records came from farmland habitat. WeBS estuary peaks in each winter were 1307 Jan and 2341 Oct. Inland WeBS peak 465 (Sep) (annual range: 216-1551; mean: 628)
F   The large flock remained at Kinneil to early Feb with 1300 present on 15 Jan and 1040 on 6 Feb. 400 Skinflats 13 Jan was the largest flock there early in the year (JC, AB). 500 returned to Kinneil by 12 Aug peaking at 831 on 16 Sep with rather low numbers from October onwards. 564 Skinflats 18 Sep and 705 on 5 Nov (DT, JC, MVB, DL).
C   137 Cambus Village Pools 3 Jul, 828 Alloa Inches 18 Sep and 1020 on 15 Oct (AET, MVB).
S   380 Lecropt 15 Jan (MVB). 1 returned to L. Dochart 7 Feb was early (NB). 244 Gart 6 Sep, 220 Blackdub 13 Oct, 120 Lecropt 16 Nov (NB, DJC, MVB).

KNOT   *Calidris canutus* (W)
   WeBS estuary peaks in each winter were 1600 Feb and 1642 Dec.
F   3940 Kinneil 13 Jan and 4000 on 30 Jan, then much smaller numbers with 1600 on 6 Feb, 195 by 13 Mar, 310 on 3 Apr. 10-16 birds remained through May to Jul with 22 on 25 May. A poor autumn with a slow build up: 100 returned by 5 Sep, 117 Kinneil 16 Oct, only 124 estuary WeBS on 5 Nov, 950 Kinneil 3 Dec (MVB, JC, CJH, GO, DT). Elsewhere 20 Blackness 18 Sep, 142 Carriden-Grangepans 16 Oct, 120 Skinflats 5 Nov, 682 on 3 Dec (AB, JC, MVB).

*LITTLE STINT   *Calidris minuta*
F   Two Skinflats 4 Sep, 1 there the following day (BTO, GO).

CURLEW SANDPIPER   *Calidris ferruginea* (p)
F   Small numbers (1-5 birds) Grangemouth area 1-18 Sep, with 5 Kinneil on 1st, 3 there next day. 2 Skinflats 4 Sep, 3 on 5th, 1 on 6th, 3 on 7th, 3 on 17th and 2 on 18th (MVB, BTO, GO, RS, DT).

Autumn passage, area summary (minimum number/half month)					
Jul		Aug		Sep	
0	0	0	0	8	3

DUNLIN *Calidris alpina* (b?,W)
Webs estuary peaks in each winter were 6263 Feb and 3540 Dec.
F   4323 Kinneil 15 Jan, 3550 on 19 Feb, 2900 Skinflats 6 Feb, 816 estuary Webs by
       13 Mar (MVB, JC, DL). No records from April to June received from the estuary.
       30 Skinflats 14 Jul and 27 Kinneil 23 Jul (AB, DT). Slow increase in numbers
       through the autumn and flocks in December were much smaller than usual. 407
       Kinneil by 16 Oct, 600 on 19 Nov, 1806 on 3 Dec. 548 Skinflats on 16 Oct, 1040
       on 5 Nov and 1650 on 3 Dec (JC, DT, MVB, DL).
S   One Gart GP 1 May (NB).
RUFF   *Philomachus pugnax* (p)
F   One winter bird, on the Carron at Skinflats, 6 Feb (MVB). A male and female
       Skinflats Pools 1 Jun (AB). In late summer/autumn present Skinflats from 25 Jul
       (1) to mid-November with maxima of 6 on 20 Aug, 8 on 5 and 9 Sep, 5 on 6 Oct
       and 6 on 11 Oct; 1 on 13 Nov the last (GO, MVB, AB, DAC, RS, DT).
C   One Cambus Pools 12 -13 Aug, 3 Tullibody Inch 18 Sep (AET).

Autumn passage, area summary (minimum number/half month)							
Aug		Sep		Oct		Nov	
3	6	9	9	6	2	2	0

*JACK SNIPE *Lymnocryptes minimus* (w)
F   Four Kinneil 4 Jan, 3 there on 22 Jan. In the second winter period Singles Kinneil
       1 Oct and 19 Nov, 4 on 26 Dec (GO, RS, DT).
S   Two Netherton marsh, Lecropt 16 Jan with 1 there 16 Oct, 2 on 18 Dec. 1 Lecropt
       6 Feb. 1 R. Forth, Allan Water to Teith confluence 20 Feb with 2 there 20 Nov. 2
       Flanders Moss 16 and 18 Mar, 1 Ashfield 7 Apr (DT, DWP).
Additions to 2004 report.
F   One St. Helens Loch 23 Oct and 15 Dec (NB).
C   One R. Devon Alva to Tillicoultry 24 Jan and 2 there on 26 Feb (EL, GL).
S   One R. Forth, Allan Water to Teith confluence 20 Feb, 1 Ashfield pools 6 Mar, 2
       Flanders Moss 3 Nov and 1 there on 16 Dec (DT, DWP).
SNIPE *Gallinago gallinago* (B,W)
       Small numbers recorded from a wide variety of wetland sites across the area but
       very few records of breeding birds.
       Only 14 birds recorded on BBS with 86 % coming from mountain and
       moorland habitat at 0.38 b/lkm. Overall numbers were 33 % above the mean
       (annual range: 3-17 birds). Inland WeBS peak 63 (Nov) (annual range: 62-140;
       mean: 99).
F   12 Kinneil 23 Feb, 10 South Alloa 4 Apr, 10 Kinneil 19 Nov and 12 St. Helens
       Loch 5 Dec were the largest numbers reported (NB, RHD, DT).
C   12 Cambus Pools 2 Jun were early returners to the low ground. 6 Cambus
       Village Pools 10 Aug; 6 Cambus Pools 20 Aug; 12 Alloa to Cambus 5 Nov. 12
       Castlebridge Business Park, Forestmill 10 Nov (AET).
S   17 Netherton marsh, Lecropt 16 Jan, 13 there on 12 Mar, 11 L. Rusky 19 Mar, 12
       Coustry Pond 23 Mar. Still 6 R. Forth, Allan Water to Teith confluence 12 May
       (NB, DT). Only two records of breeding birds, at Flanders Moss and Gartrenich
       (DWP, JM). 1 back Lecropt 21 Jul (DT). 14 L. Rusky 13 Nov, 23 on Forth near
       Kippen 16 Nov and 12 there on 7 Dec (NB, PAL).
Additions to 2004 report.
F   26 St. Helens Loch 23 Oct (NB).
S   49 Vale of Coustry 31 Oct (NB).
WOODCOCK *Scolopax rusticola* (B,W)
       Another species grossly under-recorded during the breeding season.

F   One flying across playing fields at Camelon, Falkirk 5 Jan was an unusual sighting. 1 near West Carmuirs 23 Jan, 1 Drumbowie Res. 7 Mar (MA, NB).

C   1 Gartmorn Dam 31 Mar (PMA).

S   1 Lecropt 8 Jan, 1 Flanders Moss 18 and 25 Feb and 1 Apr. 2 L.Katrine 15 Mar (MVB, DWP, SA). Summer: 4 Aberfoyle to Duke's Pass 25 Jun; 4 Duke's Pass, L. Ard Forest, 26 Jun (JT). Autumn (Oct to Dec): single birds Dunblane, L.Mahaick, R. Forth at Upper Taylorton and Strathyre; 5 Kinlochard to Stronachlachar road 15 Dec (DK, RHD, SZ, NB, DJC). A bird disturbed from a track Ardnandave forest, L. Lubnaig on 20 Nov flew c.10 m up into a Sitka Spruce from where it was disturbed again (DJC, KD).

BLACK-TAILED GODWIT *Limosa limosa* (W)
WeBS estuary peaks in each winter were 348 Feb and 380 Dec.

F   Present throughout the year at Grangemouth again. Monthly peaks at Kinneil were: 280 Jan (15th), 348 Feb (6th), 138 Mar (23rd), 86 Apr (11th), 41 May (24th), 65 Jun (9th), 137 Jul (23rd), 197 Aug (12th), 238 Sep (16th), 332 Oct (16th), 277 Nov (6th) and 180 Dec (3rd) (MVB, JC, GO, DT). Rather low numbers at Skinflats Pools again with no reports in Jan or Jun. The largest totals were 23 on 27 Mar, 55 on 25 Jul, 37 on 26 Sep and 22 on 3 Dec (MVB, AB, JC, GO, JT, DT). Elsewhere 15 Blackness 18 Sep, 37 Carriden to Grangepans 16 Oct (AB, JC). 2 South Alloa 4 Sep and 80 Kincardine Br. to Alloa 3 Dec (RHD, DM) indicate a move upriver by this species which previously has been very site faithful to Kinneil and Skinflats.

C   Five Cambus Pools 21 Apr, 6 there on 24 Apr and 1 from 10-13 Aug. Juv. Devonmouth Pool 16 Aug. 1 Cambus Village Pools 6 Sep (AET, NB, MVB).

Additions to 2004 report.

C   A good spring passage Cambus Village Pools with 1 on 17 Apr, 4 on 20th, 17 on 22nd, 19 on 23rd, 5 on 26th, 7 on 28th and 21 on 1 May (NB).

BAR-TAILED GODWIT *Limosa lapponica* (W)
WeBS estuary peaks in each winter were 93 Feb and 43 Nov.

F   Numbers were erratic at Kinneil, often under 50 birds but with some isolated much larger peaks. In the first winter period 180 on 13 Jan, 220 on 19 Feb, 50 on 21 Apr. 2 back on 1 Sep, later peaks were 140 on 1 Nov and 220 on 11 Dec (MVB, AB, JC, DT). 30 Blackness 18 Sep, 40 Airth 29 Oct (AB, JT). Very few at Skinflats as usual with 3 on 23 Apr, 8 Jul and 9 Sep, 4 on 16 Oct (MVB, AB, GO).

C   Five Kennetpans 18 Sep and 3 Dec (DL, AET).

WHIMBREL *Numenius phaeopus* (p)

F   Spring: 1 Skinflats 19 Apr, 2 on 20th and 26th, 1 on 1 May (GO, AET). Autumn: 3 W Skinflats 26 Jul, 2 there on 30th, 1 on 10 Aug, 1 on 4 Sep, 2 on 6th, 1 on 9th (AB, GO, RS, JT). At Kinneil 1 on 23 Jul, 2 on 30th, 1 on 3 Aug, 2 on 20 Aug and 2 on 16 Sep (MVB, JC, RS, DT).

S   One on Forth, Kippen 26 Apr and 27 May (MO).

Autumn passage, area summary (minimum number/half month)					
Jul		Aug		Sep	
0	5	3	3	3	2

CURLEW *Numenius arquata* (B,W)
BBS numbers were 31 % down on the mean at 0.52 b/lkm (annual range: 0.42-0.98 b/lkm) but numbers fluctuate annually with no clear pattern. They occurred at 0.91 b/lkm on mountain and moorland habitat and at 0.46 b/lkm on farmland.
WeBS estuary peaks in each winter were 1460 Jan and 1005 Sep. Inland WeBS peak 335 (Mar) (annual range: 122-623; mean 293).

F   Larger flocks than usual in January. 838 Skinflats 9 Jan, 583 on 6 Feb, 302
        Kincardine Br. to Alloa 13 Mar, 284 Kinneil 13 Jan. In the second half of the year
        545 Kinneil 23 Jul, 373 on 16 Sep, 270 on 3 Dec, 446 Skinflats 16 Oct the peak
        there, 218 Kincardine Br. to Alloa 18 Sep (MVB, JC, DL, DM, MT).

C   313 Alloa Inches 13 Jan, 284 on 6 Feb when also 204 Kennetpans. 289
        Blackgrange, Cambus 22 Jan; 120 Cambus Pools 21 Mar. 171 Kennetpans 18 Sep,
        188 Rhind, Alloa 15 Oct (AET, ACR, MT, MVB).

S   150 Lecropt 20 Feb, 166 on 11 Mar (DT). 14 Ashfield 17 Mar, 8 back Braes of
        Doune 20 Mar (DWP, DOE). 8 Lecropt 18 Aug (DT).

Addition to 2004 report.

C   292 Orchard Fm., Cambus 26 Feb (NB).

* SPOTTED REDSHANK *Tringa erythropus* (p)

F   One Blackness 20 Feb. 1 Kinneil 16 Sep (BNS, JC).

REDSHANK *Tringa totanus* (B,W)

        Recorded in very low numbers (2) on BBS; the first birds in 4 years (annual
        range: 0-4 birds). WeBS estuary peaks in each winter were 2601 Jan and 2525
        Sep.

F   Good numbers at the two main sites in both winters. 2151 Kinneil 15 Jan (when
        few at Skinflats after a SW gale), 1232 there on 6 Feb and 555 on 13 Mar. 817
        Skinflats 6 Feb, 657 there on 13 Mar. 146 Kincardine Br. to Alloa 13 Mar. 264
        Bo'ness 13 Jan (MVB, JC, DL, DM). Summer/breeding: 2 prs. Dunmore
        saltmarsh and 5, including 2 singing and display flighting, South Alloa 2 May
        (RHD). In autumn 780 Kinneil by 23 Jul, 1562 there on 16 Sep, 1253 on 16 Oct,
        1213 on 5 Nov. 740 Skinflats 16 Oct and 825 on 3 Dec. 212 Carriden to
        Grangepans 16 Sep (MVB, JC, DL).

C   121 Alloa Inches 9 Jan, 204 Kennetpans 13 Mar (AET, MT). 1 on Devon, Alva to
        Tillicoultry 20 Feb (GEL).

S   Three Ashfield 24 Mar were the first back (DWP). 8 Gart GP 2 Apr with 1 pr on
        22nd (NB, DT). 1 Balafark, Kippen Muir 3 May. 1 R. Forth, Gargunnock Br. to
        East Frew 23 Nov (RHD, AR).

GREENSHANK *Tringa nebularia* (p)

F   One or 2 birds Skinflats from the start of the year to 24 Mar, 1 Blackness 26 Jan
        and 27 Feb (MVB, AB, GO, DAC, RBA). Single birds Blackness 2 Apr, Kinneil 3
        Apr and Skinflats 11 Apr were probably on spring passage rather than
        wintering birds (DAC, DT, GO). Return passage started from late June with 1
        Skinflats 30th with 3 there on 25 Jul, 8 and 24 Aug the most, 1 or 2 during Sep,
        a wintering bird from 3 Nov to the year end with 2 on 5, 13 and 29 Nov (GO,
        MVB, AB, RS, DAC). At Kinneil 1 on 30 Jul, 5 on 16 Sep and 4 Blackness 18 Sep
        (DT, JC, AB).

C   One Cambus Pools 10-13 Aug, 2 on 20th, 3 on 24th and 1 on 3 Sep (AET).

Autumn passage, area summary (minimum number/half month)							
Jul		Aug		Sep		Oct	
0	4	4	5	3	10	1	0

GREEN SANDPIPER *Tringa ochropus* (p)

        This species is now more common as a wintering bird than a passage migrant.

F   One Carron-Bonnywater confluence 23 Jan, 1 near Carron Works 27 Mar; 1 on
        Carron, Bogston Fm. 17 Apr, 1 on flooded field between A9 and Larbert House
        19 Apr (MA). 1 Carronshore 13 Aug, 1 Skinflats 3 Sep, 2 Carronshore 31 Dec (AB,
        GO).

S   One on Teith, Forth confluence to Wester Row 23 Jan and 20 Feb, 1 Gart GP 5
        Feb (RHD, MVB).

Additions to 2004 report.
F   One Carron/Bonny Water confluence 22 Feb (MA).
C   One Cambus Village Pools 25 Jun (NB).
COMMON SANDPIPER *Tringa hypoleucos* (B)
     Recorded in very low numbers (8) on BBS, exactly the mean (annual range: 7-11 birds).
F   Return passage from 1 Jul when 1 Kinneil, 3 there 18 Jul, 2 on 23rd, 1 on 16 Sep (DT, MVB, JC). At Skinflats 2 on 12 Jul, 1 on 14th, 2 on 3 and 7 Aug, 1 on 5, 6 and 18 Sep, then a late bird on 25 Oct, 2 and 13 Nov (GO, MVB, AB, DAC).
C   One Cambus 21 Apr (AET). Return passage: 1 Cambus 3 Jul, 13 and 18 Aug, 5 Tullibody Inch 16 Jul with 2 on 6 Sep, 2 Maggie's Wood Flood, Fishcross 10-13 Aug (AET, MVB).
S   The first birds were 1 Killin 13 Apr, 1 Lake of Menteith 19 Apr, 3 on Teith, Wester Row to Doune 21 Apr, 6 Gart GP 22 Apr, 1 G. Lochay 23 Apr, 1 Ashfield and 4 Balquidder 24 Apr. Then 8 Gart GP 1 May, 5 L. Ard 6 May, 4 Killin 16 May (PWS, RAB, DWP, KP, GO, DT, NB). 5 Gart 3 and 11 Jul, 1 there on 29 Jul was the last reported inland (DT, NB). An adult with 2 very young chicks Ben Lui on 21 Jul was a late brood (DWP). A late bird at L. Ard 20 Sep (JM).

Autumn passage, area summary (minimum number/half month)									
Jul		Aug		Sep		Oct		Nov	
8	9	5	2	3	2	0	1	2	0

*TURNSTONE *Arenaria interpres* (W)
F   Four Carron mouth, Skinflats 9 Jan and 3 there on 6 Feb; 2 Carriden 13 Jan; 1 Kinneil 4 Mar, 2 there on 6 Mar (MVB, RDZ, DT). Autumn: 3 Kinneil 16 Sep, there 4 on 16 Oct and 2 on 19 Nov; 3 Blackness 18 Sep (JC, DT, AB).
*ARCTIC SKUA *Stercorarius parasiticus* (p)
F   A poor year with just three sightings: 1W Skinflats 9 Sep; 1 Carron, Grangemouth 24 Sep and 1 Kinneil 16 Oct (GO, AB, JC).
*LITTLE GULL *Larus minutus*
F   The only record was a 1st summer bird Skinflats 22 May (GO).
*MEDITERRANEAN GULL *Larus melanocephalus*
F   A 2nd winter bird west of Airth 2 and 3 Jan (RHD, AET). This was possibly the same bird seen in the same general locality in late 2004. Possibly the same bird was seen again at Powridge near Throsk 5 Jan (RS). A winter-plumaged bird Kinneil 12 Nov (DT) was considered by the local rarities committee to be very close to adult plumage.
BLACK-HEADED GULL *Larus ridibundus* (B,W)
     Numbers on BBS were 1.3 b/lkm, 27 % below the annual mean but numbers fluctuate markedly depending on what feeding flocks are encountered (annual range: 0.29-3.47 b/lkm). 91 % were found on farmland with the rest in suburban habitat. Inland WeBS peak 1135 (Jan) (annual range: 1119-2319: mean: 1445).
F   560 Skinflats 3 Aug, 7800 at the roost there 5 Nov (MVB, DL).
C   700 Blackgrange, Cambus 15 Jan (RHD).
S   Four Ashfield 28 Feb were the first back with ca.100 prs. on 3 Apr and 70 on 28 Jun but no young seen (DWP).
*RING-BILLED GULL *Larus delawarensis*
F   A 2nd winter/sub-adult bird at Kinneil 1 Oct remained to 1 Nov and was seen on the lagoon and at the mouth of the Avon. This is the first record for the area. The bird was apparently first reported on 16 Sep but DT was the only observer to submit a detailed description, which was accepted by the SBRC.

COMMON GULL Larus canus (B,W)
Recorded at the lowest density to date on BBS with 0.78 b/lkm (annual range: 0.78-8.92 b/lkm) but numbers even more dependant than Black-headed Gull on the presence/absence of feeding flocks. Recorded at roughly equal densities on mountain and moorland and farmland habitats, none from urban/suburban habitats. Inland WeBS peak 527 (Jan) (annual range: 504-2581; mean: 1255).
F   1700 Skinflats roost 5 Nov (MVB, DL).
C   Colony nesting at Hallpark, Alloa 11 May; nests and eggs destroyed by unknown persons 20 Jun. 2 chicks in nest on top of wall, Alloa Technical College annex 20 Jun. C/2 and occupied nest in grounds of demolished hospital Hallpark, Alloa 20 Jun. 8 apparently on nests at demolition site in central Alloa 28 Jun where 3 large juvs. seen. Ca. 50 nests on roof of glassworks factory, Alloa 16 Jul (NB, TC).
S   400 L.Watston 9 Jan. Several flocks of 200-400 birds noted on the Carse early in the year (DOE, DK, ACR). 4 nests Cambusmore/Gart GP 28 May (NB).
Additions to 2004 report.
C   Birds nesting at two sites in Alloa where buildings had been demolished: 51 birds, 18 apparently on nests Hallpark, Alloa 5 May, 25 there apparently on nests 17 May; 70 ads., 15 juvs. 15 Jun. A pair apparently on nest old Skol brewery site 11 May (NB).
LESSER BLACK-BACKED GULL Larus fuscus (b,S)
Small numbers winter in the Grangemouth area with occasional birds inland. Recorded in exactly the same densities as last year on BBS at 1.15 b/lkm (annual range: 0.89-1.77 b/lkm), with 92 % coming from urban/suburban habitat where feeding flocks were encountered in the Larbert/Denny area.

	Jan	Feb	Mar	Sep	Oct	Nov	Dec
Inland WeBS totals	5	0	23	125	19	52	16

F   Eight on roof of building, Camelon 8 Mar (MA). 25 nests on industrial rooftops alongside the Carron at Grangemouth 12 May with at least 30 chicks visible 8 Jun (AB). 280 Skinflats roost 5 Nov (MVB, DL).
S   65 Plean 25 Mar (RS). 111 birds of mixed ages on spring cereals Gargunnock 28 May (NB).
Addition to 2004 report.
S   An unusually large and late flock of 309 near Doune 7 Nov (NB).
HERRING GULL Larus argentatus (b,W)
As for the other gull species, numbers fluctuate in relation to the presence/absence of feeding flocks. Low numbers encountered this year, only 0.16 b/lkm against an annual mean of 0.81 (annual range: 0.1-4.17 b/lkm). Inland WeBS peak 167 (Oct) (annual range: 167-2727; mean: 604).
F   10 nesting with Lesser Black-backed Gulls on roofs alongside Carron, Grangemouth 12 May with at least 5 chicks on 8 Jun (AB). 2600 Skinflats roost 5 Nov, 800 Kinneil 4 Dec (MVB, DL, DT).
*ICELAND GULL Larus glaucoides
F   A 1st summer bird Skinflats 12-13 May (GO, AB, BTO). A 2nd summer bird Kinneil 9 Jun, 18 Jul and 19 Aug (DT) was probably the same bird as present there 18 to 25 Sep (GO, RS).
GREAT BLACK-BACKED GULL Larus marinus (S,W)
Recorded in very low numbers (2) on BBS at the mean value (annual range: 0-4 birds). Inland WeBS peak 22 (Jan) (annual range: 10-58; mean: 22)
F   33 in a field by the Carron, Camelon 9 Jan (MA) was the only double-figure flock reported.

S   A pair Gart GP 28 May and 2 Jun with 1 bird there apparently on a nest on a small islet near the water line. Failed by 17 Jun when the islet was submerged; a pair still present on 28th. (NB, DT).

*KITTIWAKE *Rissa tridactyla* (P,w)
F   One Kinneil 22 Jan and 6 Feb, 110 Blackness 13 Feb moving up the Forth, 30 Kinneil 23 Feb (DT, JC, AB). 3 Kinneil 3 Apr, 2 there on 21 Apr, 50 on 24 May (DT). 1 Kinneil 19 Aug and 27 Sep, 11 on 16 Oct (DT). An exceptional movement on 9 Sep at Skinflats when 1100+ were seen very high over the estuary before tumbling down onto the main pool, some then flying off E but most leaving SW (GO). 1 W South Alloa 27 Oct (RHD).

SANDWICH TERN *Sterna sandvicensis* (P)
F   70 Blackness 28 Aug, 20 on 18 Sep (AB). 37W high in four flocks Skinflats 5 Sep (GO).
C   One Tullibody Inch 19 Jun (JT) was an unusually early date. 7 on Forth, Cambus 12 Aug with 4 there 16 Aug (NB, AET).
S   Four Lake of Menteith on 2 Jul left high E, 20 W Fallin 6 Aug, 5 W on 29th, 8 W on 30th, 4 W, 11 E on 3 Sep, 4 SW Viewforth, Stirling 25 Aug (MW, RHD, DT).

COMMON TERN *Sterna hirundo* (B)
F   Five Skinflats 3 May with 22 there 22 May (GO). 115 Grangemouth docks 3 Aug with at least 1 chick and 8 juv (MVB). 2 Carriden-Grangepans 16 Sep, 2 Blackness 18 Sep, 1 Kinneil 16 Oct (JC, AB).
C   One on Forth, Cambus 12 Aug (NB, AET).
S   One Carron Valley Res. 30 May, 1 pr. there 6 Jun seemed to be nesting with gulls (RHD, RG, BTO, DT). 1 imm. E Lecropt 9 Aug (DT).

GUILLEMOT *Uria aalge* (W)
F   Eight Kinneil 23 Feb, 3 on 6 Mar. 2 there on 30 Jul (DT). Large numbers again in early October: 34 Kinneil 1 Oct, 120 on 8th then lower numbers; still 15 on 1 Nov, 3 on 4 Dec were the last (DT). 25 Skinflats 16 Oct, 2 there 5 Nov (MVB).
C   48 Alloa to Cambus 15 Oct, 8 Alloa Inch 17 Nov (MVB, DAC).
S   One L. Ard 20 Sep (JM).
Additions to 2004 report.
S   The October WeBS count found 15 on the R. Forth, Fallin to A91 and 9 on the A91 to A9 stretches on 17 Oct. 2 Stirling Br. to Allan Water confluence 16 Oct and One Gart GP 17 Oct (DJ, MM, GF, NB).

*RAZORBILL *Alca torda* (w)
F   Three Carriden to Grangepans 16 Oct (JC).
S   One found dead in a ditch near Lake of Menteith 27 Feb (DJC).

FERAL PIGEON *Columba livia* (B,W)
    Numbers bounced back from the all time low of 0.58 b/lkm on BBS in 2004 to 1.61 b/lkm, 30 % above the long-term mean (annual range: 0.58-2.19 b/lkm). Unsurprisingly, they occur at the highest rate in urban/suburban habitat, with 8.19 b/lkm compared to 1.63 on farmland.
S   75 Kinbuck 4 Jan and 210 there 8 Sep; 70 King's Park and Raploch, Stirling 10 Jun (NDC, MVB, ACR)

STOCK DOVE *Columba oenas* (B,W)
    Recorded in fairly low numbers on BBS transects. However, this year's total of 14 birds was the highest to date (annual range: 1-14 birds). All but one bird were registered on farmland.
F   41 Kersebrock Fm., Larbert using wild bird cover 23 Jan. 5 Kinneil 3 Apr with 2 there 23 Jul and 11 on 27 Aug (RHD, DT, MVB). Recorded Skinflats Feb, Apr, May, Jul to Sep and Nov with max of 17 Skinflats 25 Feb. 1 Bonnybridge 14 May (GO, AET, MVB, MA).

C   Eight Longcarse, Alloa 9 Jan. Singles Woodland Park, Alva 21 Apr and 6 May. 19
         (5 juvs.) Maggie's Wood Flood, Fishcross 16 Jun with up to 3 there between 13
         Aug and 5 Sep. 3 Cambus Village Pools 3 Jul and 3 Sep. 1 Alloa Inches 5 Nov
         (AET, PMA, NB).
S   Two Shrubhill, Doune 13 Jan; 2 Argaty 13 Jan with 5 there 23 Jan. 2 Old Keir,
         Lecropt 11 Feb; 2 Kippen 1 Mar (DJC). 170 Dunblane 12 Mar; 34 Plean 25 Mar;
         13 King's Park, Stirling 3 Apr; 2 Thornhill 15 Apr; 7 Hollow Burn, Fallin 24 Apr
         (MVB, RS, ACR, DK, RHD). 1 in a nestbox at Lake of Menteith 11 May was long
         dead and thought to be a juv from 2004 (RAB).

WOODPIGEON *Columba palumbus* (B,W)
         Recorded on BBS transects at 3.36 b/lkm which is 1 % above the average. It was
         recorded from all four habitat types, being most numerous on farmland at
         5.4 b/lkm and conifer woodland/moorland edge at 3.94 b/lkm.
F   300 Kinneil 23 Nov (DT).
S   An estimated 2-3,000 Carbrook Mains, Plean 4 Dec (DT).

COLLARED DOVE *Streptopelia decaocto* (B,W)
         Greatly under-reported. Numbers on BBS recovered from their all-time low last
         year to 0.32 b/lkm, their highest value ever, 24 % above the mean (annual range:
         0.17-0.32 b/lkm). Recorded in the greatest numbers in urban/ suburban areas at
         1.29 b/lkm with 0.4 b/lkm on farmland.
S   19 Doune 29 Nov (DJC).

CUCKOO *Cuculus canorus* (B)
         Occurs in low numbers on BBS transects with a total of 6 birds in 2005, a little
         below the mean (annual range: 6-17 birds). Recorded mostly in moorland
         habitat.
         First records: single Flanders Moss 29 Apr was 6 days later than in 2004 (Glen
         Buckie), which itself was 5 days later than in 2003 (DWP). This was followed by
         birds at Dalbrack, Braes of Doune, and Torrie on 30 Apr (DOE).
F   Two birds Black Loch, Slamannan in May (no specific date given). Two to three
         birds Darnrigg Moss, Slamannan 2 May and a single there 10 May with a young
         bird there begging for food from nearby Meadow Pipits (TF, RD). Singles
         Bonnybridge 18 Jun and Kinneil 11 Jul (MA, RS).
C   Singles Alva Glen 10 and 30 May; Lady Anne's Wood, Tillicoultry 11 and 30 May
         (PMA, DK, AH).
S   Single Gartrenich, Flanders Moss, 2 May, with 3 on the moss the following day.
         Two birds on 22 May, a single 8 Jun and 3 birds (one female) 16 Jun (JM, DWP,
         SRS). Singles Killin 3 and 5 May; Lock Katrine 4 May; Touch Hills 16 May, 8 and
         28 Jun; Mine Wood, BoA 21 May. Pair Dumyat 22 May. Singles L. Mahaick 24
         May; Tom Dubh 29 May and Carron Valley 30 May. Single The Vine, L. Ard
         Forest 9 Jun (RC, PM, SRS, ES, RG, EK, ASM).

BARN OWL *Tyto alba* (b,w)
         Another good run of records from the SE Stirlingshire/Clackmannanshire
         boundary and Falkirk areas following the high number of records from there
         last year. There are also a few records from outside this core area (cf. ringing
         report). The few records from the breeding season are encouraging. Maybe this
         is further evidence of the presumed recent local spread of the species.
F   One Grangemouth 7 Mar (RS). 1 found dead on barbed wire at South Alloa 29
         Oct (RHD) may have been one of the Alloa Inch birds.
C   One Devon Walk, Tillicoultry 24 and 27 Mar and 1 Alloa Inch 9 May (LN, SRS)
         are only the fourth, fifth and sixth records in Clackmannanshire in the last 25
         years.
S   Singles Dunblane 17 Jan; one hunting over verge at Castle Business Park,

Stirling 21 Jan; Torrie Wood same day; Callander 11 Feb; Westleys Fm., Lecropt 12 Feb; Kippen 18 Feb; hunting near the A9 at Ashfield 24 Feb and a female found dead on the A84 at Balquidder 25 Feb with other casualties at Forthbank, Stirling 23 and 25 Mar (RS, NB, DJC, DWP, LN). Singles Lake of Menteith 13 Apr; Balfron, 13 Apr; Lower Taylorton, Stirling 23 Apr (AS, RAB, RS). Two Gartrenich, Flanders Moss 2 May led to the erection of a nest box. Of three Y in a nesting barrel at the moss only one fledged. It is not known whether these two records relate to the same birds (JM, DWP). A bird at Doune cemetery 7 Jul was mobbed by Oystercatchers (SRS). Winter records: singles on the B826 Doune-Thornhill road 20 Oct; R. Forth near Kippen 26 Oct; Torrie Wood 28 Nov; Thornhill 21 Dec and Kepculoch Toll, Buchlyvie 31 Dec (DK, PA, DJC, JT).

TAWNY OWL *Strix aluco* (B,W)

F Single Bo'ness 7 Mar (RS).

C Birds calling Tait Place, Tillicoultry on several dates in Jan (male and female calling to each other on 22 Jan), 2 birds calling on 7 Mar, singles in Oct, Nov and several dates in Dec. Single Muckhart Mill 3 Jun. 2 large juvs Solsgirth Mine 10 Jun. Singles calling Cambus distillery on several dates in August and 3 Sep (AET, NB).

S Singles Ochiltree, Dunblane 24 Jan; R. Teith between Wester Row and Forth confluence 13 Mar; Balquhidder 24 Apr with a bird long dead at Sgiath Chuil, Crianlarich 30 Apr. Two birds Duke's Pass, Aberfoyle 25 Jun (NB, RHD, GO, MML, JT).

*LONG-EARED OWL *Asio otus* (b,w)
The larger number of records this year is encouraging.

F Remains of dead adult Dunmore Woods 24 Apr. Adult Skinflats 26 Jul (AB, GO).

C Single Naemoor Fm., Muckhart 27 Sep (JG).

S Winter records of singles Hill of Row, Dunblane 26 Jan; Dunblane 29 Nov and Muirlaggan, L. Voil 1 Dec (DOE, CO). A nest with fledged young was located at Doune Lodge, Braes of Doune 11 Jun and another nest at Flanders Moss 3 Jul (DOE).

SHORT-EARED OWL *Asio flammeus* (b,W)
For this rather local breeder, a more systematic survey of known breeding areas and potential breeding sites would be of value. No birds recorded on BBS transects.

F Singles at the traditional site of Kinneil 22 Jan and 19 Nov. Singles Black Loch, Slamannan 10 Mar and Darnrig Moss, Slamannan 24 May (DT, MA, RD).

S Singles Stronachlachar 21 Jan and in two different locations there 31 Mar (DJC). Five birds hunting at Flanders Moss 18 Feb with singles there 21 Mar, 29 Apr and 24 Oct (DWP). Singles at the feeding station, Thornhill Carse 11 Feb; Argaty, Braes of Doune 30 Mar and Forthbank, Stirling 20 Apr (DK, DOE, DRO).

*NIGHTJAR *Caprimulgus europaeus* (b)

S The breeding site at L. Ard Forest remains occupied. 1 bird was churring there 29 Jun (DA).

SWIFT *Apus apus* (B)
After last year's slump, numbers recorded on BBS recovered to the long-term mean of 0.5 b/lkm (annual range: 0.15-0.98 b/lkm) with birds being recorded in all habitats, although at greatest density in urban/suburban areas.
The first bird was recorded over Alloa 29 Apr, which is on the same day as in 2004 (Bo'ness). One was at King's Park, Stirling and 2 at Tullibody both on 30 Apr; a single over Dunblane Hydro, 3 respectively over Stirling; Gartcows (Falkirk) and Bo'ness and 6 over BoA all on 3 May, followed by 2 Aberfoyle 5 May; 2 Woodland Park, Alva 6 May; 2 Cardross 7 May; 2 River Devon at Alva

8 May and Gartmorn Dam 12 May (NB, ACR, DAC, JC, RD, SRS, RS, RHD, PMA, LI).
Autumn departures: groups of 15-20 birds moving S over Bryce Av., Carronshore 7 Aug; 5 Edgehill, BoA and Dunblane 8 Aug; 12 Gartcows, Falkirk; 5 Ashfield 10 Aug; 3 King's Park, Stirling 11 Aug and 1 Killin 19 Aug, which was 7 days earlier than in 2004 (Skinflats) (AB, CJH, MVB, NB, RD, DWP, DT, DH).

F   50 Kinneil 9 Jul (DT).

C   10 Ochil Road, Alva 1 Aug (PMA).

S   40 Flanders Moss 30 Jun; 90 Aberfoyle 8 Jul; up to 23 King's Park, Stirling 17 Jul; up to 35 Edgehill, BoA 22 Jul; 95 Carse of Lecropt 28 Jul; up to 23 Dunblane Hydro 31 Jul; 45 Carron Valley Res. 3 Aug (DT, DWP, DOE, ACR, CJH, NB).

KINGFISHER   *Alcedo atthis* (b,w)
There were seven records from the breeding season but no confirmation of breeding. The monthly max. from WeBS counts was 6 (Nov), this is 33 % below the 9-year mean of 9 (range = 5-13).

Monthly maxima from distinct sites												
D	Jan	Feb	Mar	Apr	May	Jun	Jul	Aug	Sep	Oct	Nov	Dec
F	3				1		1		5	2	3	2
C	1	2					1		1	3	5	2
S		1		4		3	1		3	3	3	1
Totals	4	3	0	4	1	3	3	0	8	8	11	5

F   R. Carron: singles Carron 30 Jan; Stirling Rd playing fields, Camelon 30 Jan; regular between M876-Larbert in autumn/winter with max. of 4 there on 18 Sep (MA). Singles Kinneil 4 Jan. 27 Sep and 19 Dec (RD, DT, GO). Singles Forth and Clyde Canal E of Bonnybridge 22 May; Union Canal, A801-aqueduct 12 Nov; R. Avon, E of Slamannan 12 Jul and R. Forth, Dunmore where feeding in small channel in saltmarsh 27 Nov (RD, KW, TF, AB).

C   One Cambus Pools 23 Feb and regular there Oct-Dec (SRS, DAC). Singles along the R. Devon, Dollar-Cambus throughout the year (DE, GEL, TC, KW, PMA).

S   Regular at Cambusmore/Gart GP throughout the year with a pr. there 2 and 7 Jun (DT, NB, MVB). 1 R. Forth, Br. of Frew - E Frew 12 Sep with 2 there on 16 Nov (PAL). R. Forth: singles R. Teith - Allan Water conf. 16 Oct; Stirling Br - Upper Taylorton 20 Nov (DT, PM). R. Teith: singles Clash, Callander 20 Jun; Doune-Wester Row 21 Apr; Carse of Lecropt 16 Oct (PAL, KP, DT). Singles R. Balvag, Strathyre 21 Oct; Ashfield 8 Sep (AEWh, BMcG, MVB).

Additions from 2003:

F   Regular on the R. Carron, M876-Larbert Sep-Nov; 1 Faughlin Res 20 Oct (MA, NB).

C   Three records R. Devon, Dollar - Alva (DE, GEL).

S   1 R. Forth, E Frew - Gargunnock Br. 9 Nov; 1 L. Ard 31 Oct; regular in Deanston lade; 1 R. Teith, Callander 11 Dec; 1 R. Lochay, Killin (PS, KF, MW, NB).

GREEN WOODPECKER   *Picus viridis* (B,W)
Remains scarce away from SE of recording area. The Killin record is the first for that locality. Only 1 bird recorded on BBS.

F   Singles Tor Wood 7 Apr and in pines there 15 Jun; Larbert hospital 11 Jun; Callendar Park, Falkirk 10 Jul. Male repeatedly seen and heard around Darnrigg Moss former opencast coal site, Slamannan, October to December (MA, AB, RS, KC, TF).

C   Seen on R. Devon at Alva in Feb, Apr, Jul, Aug and Nov. Two Woodland Park, Alva 21 Apr with singles there 6 May and 15 Jun. Single Dollar Glen 5 Jun;

Castlebridge Business Park, Forestmill 20 Jul and Alva Glen, 21 Dec (PMA, AET).
S   Singles Abbey Craig Wood, Stirling 4 Feb and 5 May; Plean CP 22 Mar and 16 Apr; Kilmahog 14 Apr; Braes of Doune, Argaty 10 Apr, 15 Jun and 12 Nov; Edinchip, Lochearnhead 27 Apr; Cocksburn Res., BoA 12 Jun; Kilbryde, Braes of Doune 15 Jun; Balquhidder 22 Jul; near Dumyat, Blairlogie 2 Oct and Achmore, Killin 20 Oct (DWP, AB, DJC, DOE, RAB, DAC, CJH, PWS).

GREAT SPOTTED WOODPECKER *Dendrocopus major* (B,W)

Recorded in small numbers (6) on BBS, which is slightly above the long term average (annual range: 0-7).

F   Records from the first part of winter were received from Skinflats 9 and 18 Mar (GO, AB). During the breeding season a pair was at Dunmore Woods 24 Apr; singles at Larbert 11 Jun; Tamfourhill, Falkirk 12 Jun; flying over Pleasance, Falkirk 13 Jun and 2 Carron Glen 14 Jun (AB, MA, KW, RDZ). Second part of winter: singles at Blackness 19 Nov; Kinneil 29 Oct, 19 Nov with 2 there 26 Nov; Skinflats and Beam Fm., Slamannan, both on 20 Nov (DAC, DT, AB, AET). Both a male and a female fed at a nut feeder Strathavon Fm., NE of Slamannan daily in Nov to 1 Dec (TF).

C   During the breeding season birds were present at Woodland Park, Alva 30 Mar with 2 there 15 Jun. Female Pond Wood, Alloa 29 Apr. Singles Dollar Glen 5 Jun; River Devon at Alva 12 Jun. Adults and 2 juvs Shelterhall, Dollar 14 Jun. Singles calling Tait Place, Tillicoultry on several dates in Jun and Jul with a juv there on 13 Jun; Castlebridge Business Park, Forestmill 28 Jul. In winter birds were present at Gartmorn Dam 16 Jan (male) with singles there 21 Sep, 18 and 24 Dec; by the R. Devon between Menstrie and Alva 21 Oct; Alloa Business Park 5 Dec and South Plantation, The Forest 14 Dec (AET, PMA, NB, DAC).

S   A M fed on peanuts in a Kippen garden throughout Jan (DAC). A F was at Dykehead, S of Lake of Menteith 28 Jan; singles SW of Doune 2 Feb; Lecropt 10 Mar, a M on a bird feeder at Alexander Drive, BoA 12 Mar; a F Plean CP 22 Mar (DAC, MVB, AB). Breeding season records were: a drumming bird Doune Ponds 23 Mar; males at Plean CP 15 Apr and Balquhidder 24 Apr; a drumming bird at Killin, W of L. Tay 3 May; singles at L. Ard 6 May; G. Lochay 6 Jun and Laighills, Dunblane 12 Aug (NB, GO, RC, GC, PWS, MVB). In the second part of winter birds were at Carron Valley Res. 6 Sep; Ashfield 8 Sep; a M Kinbuck same day; Argaty, Braes of Doune 8 Nov; Plean CP 3 Dec; a M Sommer's Lane, Blairdrummond Carse 20 Dec and a single at Gargunnock (NT, MVB, KS, AB, NB, DAC).

SKYLARK *Alauda arvensis* (B,W)

Recorded on BBS at 1.52 b/lkm, 13 % below the long-term mean (annual range: 1.25 2.71 b/lkm). Twice as frequent on mountains and moorland as in farmland. The first singing bird was at East Lundie, Braes of Doune 12 Feb followed by 4 singing birds Sheriffmuir 18 Feb; 6 Dunmore 1 Mar and 12 NW of Kippen 3 Mar (DK, DAC, AB).

F   40 Kinneil 22 Jan with 30 there 23 Feb; 120 in wild bird cover Kersebrock Fm., Larbert 23 Jan; 36 Higgins Neuk 6 Feb and 25 Skinflats 28 Oct (DT, RHD, MVB, AB).

S   66 Lecropt 15 Jan, 85 there on 23 Jan and 110 on 15 Feb (MVB, RHD).

SAND MARTIN *Riparia riparia* (B)

Numbers have varied widely on BBS but after a couple of very lean years the 2005 rate of 0.28 b/lkm is back to the long-term mean (annual range: 0.02-1.32 b/lkm). Recorded almost exclusively on farmland.

Arrival in Mar: 10 Blairdrummond GPs; 2 Craigforth, Stirling and 2 Killin Marshes all on 26th were 3 days later than in 2004 (Lake of Menteith). This was followed by 50 Quarry Loch, Blairdrummond and 40 Vale of Coustry 27th; 150 Lake of Menteith 30th and 5 L. Dochart 5th Apr (AET, RG, NB, RS, DK, DT, PWS). Departure in Aug: 1 Maggie's Wood Flood, Fishcross 24th was five days later than in 2002 (S. Alloa) - no departure dates received in 2003 and 2004 (AET). An exceptionally late bird was at Plean Tower 8 Oct (DT).

S   Ten nest holes R. Teith, Callander 20 Jun - unknown whether active or not (PAL).

SWALLOW *Hirundo rustica* (B)

The 2005 rate of 2.87 b/lkm is the highest to date, 29 % above the long-term mean, although numbers have been reasonably consistent over the years (annual range 1.65-2.87 b/lkm). It occurs with the greatest frequency in farmland at 5.06 b/lkm although the species was recorded in all habitats.

Spring arrival in Apr: 1 Carron 2nd was 9 days earlier than in 2004 (Buchlyvie) but more in line with arrival dates in previous years. This was followed by singles at Blairdrummond 7th; Callander 9th; Carse of Lecropt and Doune 10th; Carron Valley Res. 11th; 4 L. Dochart and several L. Tay, Killin 13th (AB, RHD, PH, DOE, DT, JT, PWS).

Last departures were: 2 Gartmorn Dam 21st Sep; 2 Ashfield 1st Oct; 5 Glenhead 4th Oct with the last bird Skinflats 2nd Nov. This was 2 days earlier than in 2004 (Blackness) (PMA, MVB, JS, AB).

F   112 Skinflats 11 Aug; 40 Drumbowie 14 Sep (GO, JS).
C   15+ active nests Linn Bank Fm., Dollar 7 May. 79 Cambus Pools 3 Sep (BTO, AET).
S   60 G. Dochart 28 Aug; 60 Killin 4 Sep; 70 Thornhill 18 Sep (PWS).

HOUSE MARTIN *Delichon urbica* (B)

Numbers fell for the 2nd year running on BBS and at 0.57 b/lkm was the 2nd lowest so far, being 37 % below the long-term mean (annual range: 0.25-1.7 b/lkm). Twice as common in farmland as urban/suburban habitats.

Arrivals in Apr were early again: 2 Blairdrummond 7th were 11 days earlier than in 2004 (Doune), which itself was 3 days earlier than in 2003 (L. Menteith). This was followed by singles at Blairdrummond 7th; Carron Valley Res. 11th Apr and The Gart 16th Apr (DAC, DJC, DT, DOE).

Departures in Sep were again rather early: 20 King's Park, Stirling 4th; 20 Carron Valley Res. 6th; 28 Newton Crescent, Dunblane 8th. The last records were 8 Camelon, Falkirk 3rd October and 10 Dunblane 10th Oct, which was 21 days later than in 2004 (Lecropt) and 4 days later than in 2003 (BoA) (ACR, NT, MVB, RB).

C   Ten occupied nests Coalsnaughton 22 Jul (AET).
S   Ten-15 nests Dunchroisk, G. Lochay 18 Jun with 20 prs. feeding juvs. there 29 Aug. Up to 23 King's Park, Stirling in Jun/Jul (PWS, ACR).

TREE PIPIT *Anthus trivialis* (B)

No birds were recorded on BBS for the 2nd year in a row.

Arrival in Apr: 1 Laighills, Dunblane 12th was 3 days earlier than in 2004 (Strathyre). This was followed by 2 David Marshall Lodge, Aberfoyle 19th and singles Castleton, Cowie; Drumbowie and Glen Finglas all on 23rd (MVB, DWP, RHD, PM).

C   Two singing Gartmorn Dam 12 May (PMA).
S   Two singing Carron Valley with 4 in song there 30 May. Singles Torrie 30 Apr; Flanders Moss 20 May. Birds in song Braeleny, Callander 2 Jun; David Marshall Lodge, Aberfoyle 2 Jun and Glen Finglas 3 Jun (RG, DOE, DWP, MVB).

MEADOW PIPIT *Anthus pratensis* (B,W)

At 4.16 b/lkm was only slightly below the long-term mean (annual range: 2.71-6.21 b/lkm). Continues to be scarce mid-winter.

F   Eight Skinflats 19 Feb with 18 there 5 Apr and 40 on 18 Sep. 65 Kinneil 23 Feb (AB, MVB, DT).

S   150 on passage at Stronachlachar 29 Mar; 60 Sheriffmuir 9 Apr; 40 Gart GP 24 Apr. Flocks of 110 and 120 Lecropt 4 Oct (DJC, DT, MVB).

*ROCK PIPIT *Anthus petrosus* (w)
      At traditional sites.

F   Two Dunmore 27 Oct; 1 South Alloa 29 Oct (RHD).

GREY WAGTAIL *Motacilla cinerea* (B, w)
      Recorded in low numbers on BBS; the rate this year of 0.1 b/lkm is at the top of the long-term annual range. 74 % were found on farmland with the remainder occurring on mountain and moorland. The monthly max from WeBS counts was 19 (Sep), this is 24 % below the 8-year mean of 25 (range: 16-36).

	Jan	Feb	Mar	Sep	Oct	Nov	Dec
Totals	5	8	11	26	9	11	7

F   In breeding season: pr. Carron Glen 14 Jun (RD).

C   In breeding season at R. Devon, Cambus 24 Apr. 2 ads. carried food for Y R. Devon, Muckhart Mill 16 Jun. Present in varying numbers at Maggie's Wood Flood, Fishcross 10 Aug to 9 Sep, with 5 on 16 and 17 Aug, 8 on 19 Aug, 7 on 22 Aug and 5 on 3 Sep (AET, NB).

S   In breeding season pr. R. Teith, Doune Castle 2 Apr; single L. Dochart 19 Apr; 5 R. Teith, Doune-Wester Row 21 Apr; pairs Balquhidder 24 Apr and Buckieburn Res., Denny 3 Jun. 10 Laighills, Dunblane 12 Aug; 2 Killin sewage works 25 Aug, 1 and 4 Sep (PWS, AB, MVB, RD, KP, GO).

Additions from 2003:

F   Three R. Carron, B902, Carron-Carron House 16 Feb; R. Carron, M876-B902, Carron 22 Mar and 8 there 14 Sep (AB, MA).

C   Four R. Devon, Tillicoultry-Cambus 16 Feb; 2 ads. and 3 juvs. R. Devon, Cambus 20 May; 3 R. Devon, Dollar-Tillicoultry 11 Dec. (GEL, NB, PD, KW, DE).

S   One Carrat Fm, Drip Moss 5 Jan; 1 G. Lochay at an altitude of 450m asl. 24 Jun; 5 R. Teith, Deanston-Doune Br. 26 Aug with 5 there on 12 Sep and 6 on 16 Oct (NB, DC, MW).

PIED WAGTAIL *Motacilla alba* (B, w)
      Numbers on BBS recovered a little from last year's low point to 0.35 b/lkm, still 21 % below the mean (annual range: 0.21-0.77 b/lkm), however. Recorded in all habitats apart from urban/suburban with the highest density occurring on farmland at 0.63 b/lkm. An increasing number of White Wagtails (*Motacilla alba alba*) are being recorded away from coastal locations.
      Scarce in winter. Fewer winter records were received this year compared to previous years, especially from the second part of winter. 4 Jan records (4 in 2004): single Delph Pond, Tullibody 4 Jan; 51 at roost in Falkirk centre 8 Jan; singles Kippen centre 21 Jan and Blackness 26 Jan. Only 1 Feb record (2 in 2004): 10 Skinflats 19 Feb (NB, DAC, AB, GO). 6 Nov records (4 in 2004): singles Gartmore Pond 13 Nov; Tullibody 16 Nov; Hillend Fm., Slamannan 20 Nov; The Meadows, Callander and Vale of Coustry both on 24 Nov; Castlebridge Business Park, Forestmill 28 Nov. Only 6 Dec records (10 in 2004): singles R. Forth at Alloa Inch 4 Dec; Alloa centre 14 Dec; Tait Place, Tillicoultry 25 Dec with 2 there 27 Dec; Tullibody 29 and 31 Dec (NB, AET, DAC).

F   Three White Wagtails Skinflats 20 Apr (MA, AET).

C   Present in varying numbers (mostly juvs.) at Maggie's Wood Flood, Fishcross 13 Aug to 19 Sep, with 10 on 19 Aug, 11 on 13 Aug and 9 Sep and 12 on 26 Aug.

S   Present in varying numbers at King's Park, Stirling 17 Jul to 8 Sep. Numbers gradually increased as juveniles joined the adults, with 31 birds on 7 Aug, 26 on 30 Aug, 42 on 5 Sep and 100 birds on 8 Sep (ACR). 10 Killin sewage works 25 Aug and 6 there 1 Sep (PWS). Single White Wagtail Carron Valley Res. 11 Apr and 6 White Wagtails Cambusmore/Gart 1 May (DT, NB).

WAXWING *Bombycilla garrulus* (w)
         Not surprisingly, after last year's invasion birds were still encountered in a few locations at the start of the year, albeit in smaller numbers. There were a handful of sightings away from the conurbations in the SE of the recording area. Two birds seen at Argaty had been ringed in Aberdeenshire (cf. Ringing Report). Few birds returned in the second part of the winter.

F   41 Airth 2 Jan; 6 Bo'ness 6 Jan; 7 Skinflats 15 and 16 Jan; 20 Stenhousemuir 26 Mar (BNS, MA, RS, AB). At the end of the year 11 Falkirk 17 Dec with 21 there 23 Dec; 20 Polmont 26 Dec (BTO, JT).

C   11 Dollar Road, Tillicoultry 3 Jan were in same garden as in 2001; 6 R. Devon at Alva 30 Jan (AET, PMA).

S   20 flying S at Strathyre 1 Jan; 2 Fallin 4 Jan; 14 W of Kippen 13 Jan with 27 there 19 Jan; 9 Argaty, Braes of Doune 17 and 18 Jan. At the reliable site of Stirling Royal Infirmary there were 36 birds on 25 and 26 Jan. 25 still Springkerse, Stirling 4 Feb and 10 Wellpark Crescent, Stirling 18 Feb. 35 Doune 5 Feb; 1 BoA 15 and 18 Mar (DJC, RHD, NB, DOE, AB, DAC, BNS, DC). The first birds of the second part of winter were 20 Port of Menteith 22 Oct, followed by 7 Dunblane 10 Nov and 8 on 16 Nov (DOE, RB, NB).

DIPPER   *Cinclus cinclus* (B,W)
         As usual, recorded in low numbers on BBS with 4 birds, the same as the long-term mean (annual range: 1-11).

	Jan	Feb	Mar	Sep	Oct	Nov	Dec
WeBS Inland Totals	18	33	23	21	18	27	32

F   Max. 4 R. Carron, M876-Carron House (10.8km) Feb and Mar; max. 5 Sep and Oct (MA, AB).

C   Max. 11 R. Devon, Dollar-Tillicoultry (6.1km) 28 Jan and 15 on 30 Nov; 6 (3 prs.) R. Devon, Tillicoultry-Alva (5.3km) 12 Mar and 6 there on 16 Sep; 5 R. Devon, Tullibody Br -A 907 (2.6km) 17 Oct (DE, GEL, KW).

S   Five R. Teith, Lanrick (4.4km) 6 Feb (DOE).

Additions from 2003:

F   Max. 6 R. Carron, M876-Larbert (3.7km) 13 Feb with 8 on 16 Nov (MA).

C   Max. 16 R. Devon, Dollar-Tillicoultry (6.1km)13 Feb with 13 on 7 Nov; 5 R. Devon, Tullibody Br.-A 907 (2.6km) 16 Oct (DE, KW).

S   5 R. Teith, Deanston-Doune Br 12 Jan; 8 R. Teith, Lanrick (4.4km) 25 Oct; max. 6 Allan Water, Ashfield-Dunblane (4.4km) 31 Jan; 6 Allan Water, BoA-Cornton (1.2km) 16 Nov (MW, DOE, AW, JM).
         Breeding: recently fledged juv. on steep hillside G. Lochay 24 Jun (DC).

WREN   *Troglodytes troglodytes* (B,W)
         Widespread and common. Under-recorded.
         Occurs on BBS with 2.78 b/lkm, 30 % above the long-term mean and the highest rate yet recorded. (the annual range is quite narrow at 1.53-2.78 b/lkm). Density is at its highest in coniferous woodland but this species is recorded in all habitats.

F   Ad. and 3 juvs. Bo'ness garden 28 Jun (AS).

C   11 Cambus Pools 19 Apr; 10 Gartmorn Dam 12 May; 12 Alva Glen 30 May (ACR, PMA, DK).

S   10 Hollow Burn, Fallin 24 Apr; 6 King's Park, Stirling 25 Apr (RHD, ACR).
DUNNOCK *Accentor modularis* (B,W)
Widespread and common. Under-recorded.
Recorded at its highest level to date on BBS with 0.76 b/lkm (annual range: 0.34-0.76). Numbers were roughly equal in all habitats except for mountain and moorland where there were none.
F   Albino bird from last year reappeared in Carronshore garden 27 Oct (AB).
C   Ten R. Devon, Alva 13 Mar (PMA).
ROBIN *Erithacus rubecula* (B,W)
Under-recorded. Occurs on BBS locally with 1.39 b/lkm, 11 % above the long-term mean (annual range: 0.92-1.43). Found in all habitats but at greatest density in coniferous woodland, 2.5 b/lkm and urban/suburban, 2.07 b/lkm with only 1.69 b/lkm in farmland.
C   10 to 12 birds recorded Gartmorn Dam Feb to Oct; 10 Alva Glen 30 May (ACR, PMA, DK).
S   13 to 15 birds King's Park, Stirling Feb to Apr. One of two birds there eating Elderberries 2 Sep. 24 Carron Valley Res. 6 Sep (ACR, NT).
*BLACK REDSTART *Phoenicurus ochruros*
Vagrant to the recording area.
S   M on access track to Earl's Hill 23 Mar (GEL). This is only the 4th record for the recording area.
REDSTART *Phoenicurus phoenicurus* (B)
A good showing during the breeding season this year. Occurs in very low numbers on BBS transects with only 2 this year. Recorded for the first time in 2003 (annual range: 2-5).
Arrival in Apr: one singing Dun Dubh, Aberfoyle 19th was 9 days earlier than in 2004 (Killin). This was followed by Ms at Doune Lodge, Braes of Doune 23th and Balquhidder 24th; a single Flanders Moss 29th and a M Lanrick 30th (DT, DOE, DWP).
F   One Skinflats 8 Jul (AB).
S   One Flanders Moss 2 May, with 3 Ms there 6 and 10 May and 1 M 20 May. One singing near Townhead Fm., N. Third Res. and 2-3 singing Mains of Glinns, Kippen both 3 May. 1 L. Ard 6 May. Males Bracklinn, Callander 14 May; Lanrick and Buchany, Braes of Doune both 15 May. Singles L. Tay, Killin 16 and 24 May; Deanston 7 Jun (JM, DWP, RHD, GC, DOE, PWS, SRS).
WHINCHAT *Saxicola rubetra* (B)
Occurs in very low numbers on BBS transects with only 2 birds in 2005 (annual range: 2 -21 birds), the lowest annual total to date
The early spring arrival has been remarkably consistent over the last three years: 1 Carron Valley 30 Apr was a day earlier than in 2004 (Flanders Moss) and in 2003 (Gartrenich, Aberfoyle). This was followed by a single Flanders Moss 3 May, with 3 Ms there at High Moss Pow 13 May; 3 upstream of Kinbuck Bridge 4 May; a M Lundie, Braes of Doune 7 May; 2 Ms Drumbane, Braes of Doune and 4 Ms Carron Valley all on 14 May (RG, DWP, MVB, DOE, GO)
Autumn departure: 1 South Alloa 28 Aug. 2 Kinbuck 8 Sep were 10 days later than in 2004 (Lecropt) but 10 days earlier than in 2003 (also Lecropt). A late bird Skinflats 11 Oct (RHD, MVB, RS).
F   Two Skinflats 10 Jul, with a M there 21 Jul and 2 birds 11 Aug (RS, GO).
S   Six bottom of Dumyat 22 May; 2 prs. Carron Valley 30 May; 1 Gartrenich, Flanders Moss 8 Jun; 4 Flanders Moss 4 Jun (SRS, RHD, RG, BTO, JM). Pr. feeding 4 Y Auchlyne Rd., G. Dochart 3 Jul, with a pr. and 7Y there still 7 Sep. Pr. G. Lochay 4 Jul. 5 Carse of Lecropt 21 Jul (PWS, DT).

STONECHAT *Saxicola torquata* (b,w)
Local BBS numbers were the highest to date, having risen steadily from 0.01 b/lkm in 1997 to 0.14 b/lkm this year. As would be expected, they were found solely in mountain and moorland habitat.

F   One to two birds Skinflats 16 and 21 Jan, 12 and 18 Mar (pr.), various dates in Jun (pr.), various dates in Jul where pr. and 3 imms. on 5th, M 13th, prs. 5 Sep and 2 Nov (MA, AB, GO, DT). 2 F Kinneil 22 Jan with 3 birds there 16 Oct, 2 on 29 Oct, up to 2 on various dates in Nov and M 26 Dec (DT, MVB, GO). M Darnrig Moss, Slamannan 10 May. M and 3 juvs. Tamfourhill, Falkirk 21 Jun (RDZ).

S   Females Carse of Lecropt 8 Jan and near Brig o' Turk 22 Jan. Pr. E of Thornhill 1 and 10 Feb. Single L. Rusky 5 Feb. Pr. Sheriffmuir 12 Feb with 2M and 1 F there 18 Feb and several birds 12 May. Pr. near Stronachlachar 20 Feb. Pr. Drumloist, Braes of Doune 2 Apr (DT, DAC, DK, DOE). F Bovain, G. Dochart 26 Mar. M Auchlyne, G. Dochart 23 Apr with a pr. there 3 Jul and a pr. and one juv. 11 Aug. At an unspecified location in G. Dochart pr. and 4 juvs. 28 Jul and 2 Aug; 2 prs. there 16 Oct and 2 prs. and 1 Y 17 Oct. Pr. and Y Dunchroisk, G. Lochay 29 Aug with 1 there 23 Nov (NB, PWS). One Carron Valley 3 May with 2 ads. and 2 juvs. there 14 May and 2 ads. 30 May. Pr. Flanders Moss 13 May; 3 Tom Dubh, Callander 27 May with 2 there 29 Jun. 5 Cromlix Moor 4 Jul (NT, RG, DWP, ES, DWP). 3 birds Carron Valley Res. 6 Sep with M there 20 Sep and several birds 15 Oct (GO, DAC). Pr. Kippen Muir Dam 20 Sep; single Dumyat 2 Oct; pr. Polmaise landfill site, Fallin 27 Oct (DAC, RHD).

WHEATEAR *Oenanthe oenanthe* (B)
The 0.15 b/lkm recorded this year on BBS is exactly that of the long term mean (annual range: 0.07-0.25 b/lkm). All but one bird occurred in mountain and moorland habitat.

Spring arrival: One M and 2 F Arnprior 21 Mar were 5 days earlier than in 2004 (Kinneil). This was followed by 2 Ms Bows, Braes of Doune 24 Mar; F Drumloist, Braes of Doune 3 Apr; single L. Voil 7 Apr; pr. in ploughed field Hartsmailing, Fallin; 2M and 1 F Carse of Lecropt 10 Apr; F Kinneil 11 Apr (DJC, DOE, RG, RHD, DT).

Autumn departure: singles Skinflats 1 and 5 Sep; Kinneil 5 Sep. This is a month later than in the same locations in 2001 (no departure dates received for 2002-04) (MVB, DT).

F   Migrants: Pr. Skinflats 23 Apr with 5 S of Howkerse Fm., Skinflats Village 1 May; M and 3F on Skinflat Pools 3 May and 5 at pools 6 May; 2 Airth shore, Dunmore saltmarsh and 2 South Alloa all on 2 May were believed to possibly be of Greenland race *leucorhoa*; 2 Bowtrees, Airth 6 May; 2 Kinneil 2 Aug (AB, AET, GO, RHD, DT).

C   Migrants: Single The Rhind, Alloa 24 Apr; 2 Balhearty Fm., Coalsnaughton 6 May. 1 Alva Glen 30 May (AET, DK).

S   Single Sgiath Chuil, Crianlarich 30 Apr. Records from the first week of May were received from Killin, W of L. Tay ('many') on 3rd; Flanders Moss (4) on 3rd; N. Third Res. (3) on 3rd; Carron Valley (3) on 4th with 1 there 30th; Hollow Burn, Fallin; Gogar Loan; Ashfield; Townhead Fm.; Cringate Moor (6) all on 8th; 2 females Thornhill Carse 17th May (MML, RG, DWP, RHD, RC, GO). Pr. and Y G. Lochay 4 Jul. 1 Ashfield 6 Aug (PWS, DWP).

*****RING OUZEL** *Turdus torquatus* (b)
S   Pr. Beinn nan Eachan, Killin 3 May. 1 Ben Lui 21 Jul (RC, DWP).

BLACKBIRD *Turdus merula* (B,W)
Recorded on BBS at 2.63 b/lkm, 10 % above the long-term mean. Annual numbers have been in a very narrow range of 1.82-2.72 b/lkm. As usual, the

urban/suburban habitat was most favoured by this species with 6.81 b/lkm, although this was the lowest rate since BBS began, 35 % down on the 11 year mean. This fall was more than compensated for with a rise of 23 % to 3.68 b/lkm on farmland (many more squares covered) and 1.31 b/lkm in conifer woodland/conifer moorland edge, double the mean rate. No birds were recorded in the mountain/moorland habitat.

S   Up to 19 King's Park, Stirling between 9 May and 28 Jun (PMA, GM). 6 BoA fed on Cotoneaster berries 30 Nov and 1 Dec (CJH). 23 Gartmorn Dam 7 Dec (RHD).

FIELDFARE *Turdus pilaris* (W)

Spring departure in Apr: 100 Thornhill 5th; 300 Cromlix 9th; 4 Auchinlay, Dunblane 12th; single Skinflats 14th. 20 Flanders Moss 29th was 11 days later than in 2004 (Lodge, Braes of Doune) (DOE, GO, MVB, DWP).

Autumn arrival in Oct: 100 Glenhead 20th was 3 days later than in 2004 (Lodge, Braes of Doune). This was followed by 12 R. Devon, Menstrie-Alva 21st; 35 SW at Lerrocks 27th; flocks in G. Dochart 28th and 100 Doune 29th (MVB, PWS, DOE).

F   200 Kinneil 26 Nov and 80 there 19 Dec; 52 Skinflats 3 Dec (JS, GO, DT, MVB).

C   70 R. Devon, Alva 30 Jan and 35 there 11 Dec (PMA).

S   As traditionally, the Carse of Lecropt attracted large numbers with 273 on 4 Jan, 1,000 there 8 Jan, 295 on 9 Nov and 250 on 20 Nov (NB, DT, MVB). 150 Dykes, Fallin 2 Jan; 220 Thornhill Carse 20 Jan and ca. 400 there at Myme Farm 21 Jan; 80 old railway, Kippen 24 Jan; 65 Baad Farm, Drip Carse 29 Jan; 80 S Flanders Road, Kippen 3 Mar (RS, DJC, DAC, DK). 260 Rossburn Lane, Blairdrummond 3 Dec; ca. 200 Drip Moss 17 and 25 Dec; 70 Nether Carse, Thornhill Carse 18 Dec; ca. 70 R. Forth, Gargunnock 20 Dec; 70 Gartmore and 100 Kippen both 27 Dec (MVB, DAC, ACR, TR, JT).

SONG THRUSH *Turdus philomelos* (B,W)

Under-recorded. Recorded at 0.78 b/lkm towards the top end of the annual range (0.46-0.82 b/lkm) and 22 % up on the 8-year mean. It was found in all four major habitat types at densities close to the annual means.

As usual, few winter records. January records: single R. Devon, Alva 2nd; 2 singing Kinneil 14th; singles singing West Mains Pond and Larbert House, Falkirk 15th; singles Woodland Park, Alva 18th; Alva Glen 24th. 2 King's Park, Stirling 29th; single Kippen 31st. One on various dates in Jan, Feb and Dec in Dunblane garden. One on various dates in Feb to Apr in Bo'ness garden with 2 there 29 Mar. 8 R. Devon, Menstrie-Alva 23 Nov with 2 there 6 and 15 Dec and a single 23 Dec. 1 Gartmorn Dam 7 Dec (PMA, DAC, MA, ACR, NB, AS).

F   One singing Skinflats 18 Mar (AB).

C   Eight R. Devon, Alva 13 Mar (PMA).

S   11 Kippenrait, Dunblane 12 Mar; 5 King's Park, Stirling 17 Mar; 2 singing Plean CP 22 Mar; 5 L. Voil 7 Apr; 7 Hollow Burn, Fallin 24 Apr; 2 Killin 28 May; 3 Killin, L. Tay 18 Jun; 5 SW Newton Crescent, Dunblane 22 Sep (MVB, AB, ACR, RG, RHD, PWS).

REDWING *Turdus iliacus* (W)

Spring departure: 20 Dalrigh, Tyndrum 13 Apr (JT) was 4 days earlier than in 2004 (Lodge, Braes of Doune).

Autumn arrival in Oct: 1 Argaty, Braes of Doune 8th was 12 days later than in 2004 (Kilbryde, Braes of Doune). This was followed by 2 SW Newton Crescent, Dunblane 9th; 28 Doune and 88 Argaty both on 14th; 40 Carse of Lecropt 16th; 300 Skinflats 19th (MVB, DT, AB).

F   Largest flock was 50 Kinneil 19 Nov (DT).

C   Largest flocks were 40 R. Devon, Alva 2 Jan with 40 there 21 Oct and 50 on 11 Dec (PMA, DAC).
S   Largest flock at traditional site of Lecropt was 200 on 8 Jan. 120 west of Kippen 13 Jan; 85 Kippenross, Dunblane 12 Mar (DT, DAC, MVB). 120 Lerrocks, Braes of Doune 27 Oct with 110 there 10 Nov; 45 Doune 2 Dec; 50 Gartmore 27 Dec; ca. 70 Mosslaird, Ochertyre Moss 20 Dec (MVB, JT, NB).
MISTLE THRUSH *Turdus viscivorus* (B,W)
        Greatly under-recorded. Recorded at 0.25 b/lkm on BBS, 32 % above the long-term mean (annual range: 0.07-0.3 b/lkm). Spread fairly evenly across all four major habitat groups at densities close to the annual means with a slight bias towards mountain, moorland and conifer habitats.
C   Ten Maggie's Wood Flood, Fishcross 1 Sep (AET).
S   Two Stirling Royal Infirmary 25 Jan chased off Waxwings. 15 Nether Carse, Thornhill Carse 18 Dec. Ca. 24 R. Forth, Gargunnock (AB, ACR, TR).
*GRASSHOPPER WARBLER *Locustella naevia* (b)
        Only one bird recorded on BBS (annual range: 1-4 birds).
        Spring arrival: 1 Skinflats 23 Apr was same date as in 2004 at same location and a day earlier than in 2003 (Ashfield, Dunblane). This was followed by 2 Flanders Moss 29 Apr; 2 Carron Valley 30 Apr; singles Hollow Burn, Fallin and Airth shore 2 May; 4 singing High Moss Pow, Flanders Moss 3 May (AB, DWP, RG, RHD).
F   At Skinflats 26 Apr, 3 May and 14 Jul. 2 singing Standburn, Falkirk 28 Jun (GO, RHD).
C   Two Blackgrange 9 Jul (DRO).
S   Five singing Duke's Pass, Aberfoyle 26 Jun (DT).
SEDGE WARBLER *Acrocephalus schoenobaenus* (B)
        After last year's high of 17 birds, only 4 were recorded on BBS locally this year, the lowest ever (annual range: 4-17).
        Spring arrival: several R. Devon, Alva-Menstrie 30 Apr was 1 day earlier than in 2004 (Blairdrummond and Rhind, Alloa). This was followed by 4 Skinflats 3 May which gradually increased to 12 singing birds by 15 May. 2 upstream of Kinbuck Bridge 4 May (DAC, GO, AB, MVB).
        Autumn departure: 1 Tullibody Inch 6 Sep was 9 days later than in 2004 (Kinneil) and 26 days later than in 2003 (Skinflats) (MVB).
        Birds faithful to Skinflats and Cambus Pools sites.
F   Ad. and 4 Y Kinneil 2 Jun (AB).
C   Three Gartmorn Dam 12 May; 6 Blackgrange, Cambus 9 Jul (PMA, DRO).
WHITETHROAT *Sylvia communis* (B)
        The BBS rate of 0.26 b/lkm was 24 % up on the long-term mean (annual range: 0.09-0.32 b/lkm).
        Spring arrival: 1 Castleton, Cowie and several R. Devon, Menstrie-Alva 30 Apr were 7 days later than in 2004 (Skinflats). This was followed by singles Hollow Burn, Fallin; South Alloa and Skinflats 2 May with 4 at the latter site 3 May (RHD, DAC, AB, GO).
        Autumn departure: 2 Laighills, Dunblane 13 Aug; 2 R. Devon, Alva 14 Aug and 2 Ashfield, Dunblane 8 Sep (MVB, PMA).
C   Single R. Devon, Alva 8 May and 12 Jun with 4 there 10 Jul. 2 Gartmorn Dam 12 May, 30 Jun and singles 19 Jul and 9 Aug. 1 Cambus Pools 5 Jul with 6 Blackgrange, Cambus 9 Jul (PMA, ACR, DRO).
GARDEN WARBLER *Sylvia borin* (B)
        Recorded in very low numbers on BBS transects with wide annual fluctuations. This year's total of 6 birds is the highest to date (annual range: 0 -6).

Spring arrival in May: 1 Fallin 2nd was 3 days later than in 2004 (Devon Walk, W of Dollar). This was followed by one bird Kinbuck, Dunblane and 2 Solsgirth Mine, NE of Forest Mill 4th; a single Doune 8th; 4 King's Park, Stirling 9th with 2 there 30th and 7th Jun(RHD, MVB, NB, DOE, ACR).
No autumn departure dates were received.

C   Singles R. Devon, Alva 12 Jun; Gartmorn Dam 30 Jun and 19 Jul (PMA).

S   One singing Bracklinn Falls, Callander 2 Jun (MVB).

BLACKCAP *Sylvia atricapilla* (B)

This year's rate of 0.18 b/lkm was 29 % up on the mean (annual range: 0.07-0.19 b/lkm). The highest rate occurred in the conifer and conifer/moorland edge habitat with 0.38 b/lkm. There were 0.26 b/lkm in the urban/suburban areas and 0.2 b/lkm on farmland.

Winter records: no birds were observed during the first part of winter. In the second part: F R. Devon, Menstrie-Alva 21 Oct; M in Carron garden feeding on *Pyracantha* 4 Nov. Immature moulting M on feeder Alexander Dr., BoA 11 Dec; M Ochiltree, Dunblane 19 Dec (DAC, AB, MVB, NB).

Spring arrival in April: singles Blairlogie and Cambus Pools 10th were 1 day later than in 2004 (Falkirk). This was followed by male Laighills, Dunblane and 2 birds Gartmorn Dam 12th. Singing male Skinflats 13th with 2 males there 19th. Reported from several sites in Falkirk and Clackmannanshire from 21st onwards (DAC, PMA, MVB, GO).

Autumn departure: no records received.

F   One Skinflats 21 Apr with 2 there 23 Apr, Ms on 3 and 6 May and 3 birds on 12 May. 1 R. Devon, Alva 8 May and 2 there 10 Jul. 7 Gartmorn Dam 12 May with 4 there 30 Jun and 2 on 9 Aug (GO, GM, AB, PMA).

C   Single Woodland Park, Alva 21 Apr with 2 there 6 May and 6 on 20 Jul (PMA).

S   Five Hollow Burn, Fallin 24 Apr. Singles King's Park, Stirling 11 May with 3 there 10 Jun and 1 on 28 Jun. Singles Allan Water, Dunblane 20 Jun and 8 Jul. 3 juvs. Laighill, Dunblane 12 Aug (RHD, ACR, PMA, MVB).

WOOD WARBLER *Phylloscopus sibilatrix* (B)

Under-recorded. As usual, only one bird was recorded on BBS.

C   One singing Dollar Glen 5 Jun (AET). This is the last known occupied site in Clackmannanshire.

S   1 Sgiath Chuil, Crianlarich 30 Apr. 5 singing Glen Finglas 3 Jun (MML, MVB).

CHIFFCHAFF *Phylloscopus collybita* (B)

Overall numbers were small with a total of 19 birds. This was down 29 % on last year's high of 0.17 b/lkm but close to the rate for the last 3 years (annual range: 0.01-0.22 b/lkm). Numbers were highest in urban/suburban squares with 0.73 b/lkm compared to 0.28 b/lkm on farmland, the only other habitat they were recorded in.

Spring arrival: singles Blairlogie and original Union Canal tunnel, Falkirk 24 Mar were 1 day later than in 2004 (Ashfield). This was followed by 2 Blair-drumond and 1 singing Laighills, Dunblane 25 Mar with 2 singing at the latter site 12 Apr; 2 Plean CP 29 Mar with 5 singing there 15 Apr; 1 singing Ashfield and 1 Stirling 2 Apr (DAC, RDZ, DWP, DOE, AB, GO, DOE).

Autumn departure: no records received.

F   Several birds Dunmore Woods 24 Apr (AB). 1 Skinflats 28 Nov was probably an overwintering bird (GO).

C   During breeding season reported from Comely Bank Wood, Alloa and Cambus (NB, RDZ).

S   Single singing Bracklinn Falls, Callander 2 Jun. Overwintering birds: 1 Carse of Lecropt 20 Nov and 1 BoA 1 Dec (MVB, DT, CJH).

WILLOW WARBLER　*Phylloscopus trochilus*　(B)
　　　There has been a steady decline locally since 1997 with this year's rate of 1.23
　　　b/lkm being 57 % below that of 1997 and 33 % below the mean. The highest rate
　　　occurred in the conifer and conifer/moorland edge habitat with 3.56 b/lkm
　　　although it was recorded in all four main habitat types.
　　　Spring arrival in April: 1 Fallin Bing and Doctor's Wood and 1 singing Flanders
　　　Moss 3rd were 13 days earlier than in 2004 (Lecropt and Blairdrummond). This
　　　was followed by a single Allan Water, Dunblane and 8 King's Park, Stirling 11th;
　　　3 singing Dunblane and 3 Gartmorn Dam 12th with birds reported from many
　　　locations from mid-month (RHD, PMA, MVB, ACR).
　　　Autumn departure in September: 5 Carron Valley Res. 6th; 3 Ashfield 8th;
　　　singles Skinflats and Newton Crescent, Dunblane 18th; 1 Gartmorn Dam 21st.
　　　A late bird 6 Oct Allan Water, Dunblane was 27 days later than in 2001 (no dates
　　　available for 2002-2004) (NT, MVB, PMA).
F　　　Two Skinflats 14 Apr rose to 7 on 21 Apr with 4 there 23 Apr. 6 Hollow Burn,
　　　Fallin 24 Apr (GO, GM, AB, RHD).
C　　　Four singing Cambus Pools 24 Apr with 1 still there in sub-song 18 Aug; 18
　　　Gartmorn Dam 12 May with 16 there 9 Aug (AET, PMA).
GOLDCREST　*Regulus regulus*　(B,W)
　　　Under-recorded. Few notable records were received.
　　　Recorded at its highest level to date on BBS with 1.07 b/lkm (annual range: 0.18-
　　　1.07). The 2005 rate is 8 % up on that of 2004 and 73 % above the mean.
F　　　12 Skinflats 30 Jan. Many pairs now established in young Fir trees in mixed
　　　plantation on former opencast site at Darnrigg Moss (MA, TF).
S　　　147 Carron Valley Res. 6 Sep (NT).
SPOTTED FLYCATCHER　*Muscicapa striata*　(B)
　　　Recorded in very low numbers on BBS with the 5 birds this year equalling the
　　　average (annual range: 2- 12). Remains scarce with reports from 23 locations
　　　received. Spring arrival in May: single G. Dochart 14th was 2 days later than in
　　　2004 (Killin shore). This was followed by 2 Muckhart Mill 26th; singles
　　　Strathavon Fm., Slamannan 24th; NE Dollar 29th; Devon Walk, Dollar and
　　　Harviestoun, Tillicoultry 31st (RHD, RDZ, DT).
　　　No autumn depature data were received.
C　　　Singles Dollar Glen 5 Jun; Shelterhall, Dollar 14 Jun; Foulbutts Wood, Solsgirth
　　　10 Jun; 4 Y Muckhart Mill 14 Jun (AET, NB).
S　　　Single Brig o' Turk 3 Jun with 2 there 24 Jul. Pr. G. Lochay power station 4 Jun;
　　　4 Glen Lochay 6 Jun with 1 there 18 Jun, several there 4 Jul and 4 in the lower
　　　reaches on 28 Jul. Singles Dochart Bridge, Killin 29 Jun; Auchlyne Rd., G.
　　　Dochart 2 Jul and 2 there 11 Aug. Pr. raised br/3 Blairdrumond 3 Jul; Y heard
　　　calling in nest Lochearnhead 4 Jul. Pr. raised br/2 Inverardoch 21 Aug (MVB, DT,
　　　PWS, RDZ, DOE, DJC). Elsewhere reported from Aberfoyle 3 Jun; Buchany,
　　　Braes of Doune 6 Jun; Bows, Braes of Doune 21 Jun; 2 Ardenoaig, L. Tay 24 Jun;
　　　pr. Killin, L. Tay 7 Aug; single Ashfield, Dunblane 12 Aug (MVB, DOE, PWS).
*PIED FLYCATCHER　*Ficedula hypoleuca*　(b)
S　　　One Glen Finglas 22 Apr; male Bracklinn Falls, Callander 14 May; pr. G. Lochay
　　　4 Jun (PM, DOE, DT).
LONG-TAILED TIT　*Aegithalos caudatus*　(B,W)
　　　Numbers on BBS fluctuate markedly (annual range: 0.03-0.38) with the 2005
　　　returns the lowest ever at only 0.03 b/lkm, 82 % below the mean.
F　　　12 Skinflats 18 Sep. 6 in woodland regeneration Langlees, Falkirk 28 Oct (MVB,
　　　AB).
C　　　Flocks over 10 birds or more were 14 Gartmorn Dam 2 Feb with 16 there 7 Dec;

10 Woodland Park, Alva 11 Feb. 15 Cambus Pools 14 Mar with 7 there incl. 1 juv. 2 Jun and 12 on 20 Aug. 5 Comely Bank Wood, Alloa 24 May incl. 2 juvs. being fed by ads. (PMA, ACR, AET, NB).

S   12 Killin Marshes 10 Jan; 15 Lecropt 15 Jan. Nest Achray Water 6 May (NB, MVB, RHD).

COAL TIT *Parus ater* (B,W)

Widespread but under-recorded. The BBS rate of 0.91 b/lkm was 36 % above the mean (annual range: 0.32-1 b/lkm). Found at much higher densities in coniferous woodland than elsewhere, 5.19 b/lkm compared to 0.37 on farmland squares.

S   One singing Ochiltree, Dunblane 7 Jan (NB).

BLUE TIT *Parus caeruleus* (B,W)

Under-recorded. The 2005 rate of 2.51 b/lkm was the highest to date (annual range: 1.2-2.51 b/lkm), some 31 % above the previous high and 44 % up on the mean. This increase is mostly due to its increase in farmland, where this year's rate of 4.3 b/lkm is the highest yet, 48 % above the mean.

S   One singing Ochiltree, Dunblane 19 Jan; 22 Cardross 7 May; 17 Carron Valley Res. 6 Sep (NB, LI, NT).

GREAT TIT *Parus major* (B,W)

Under-recorded. This year's figure of 1.14 b/lkm is a new high, 54 % up on the mean (annual range: 0.41-1.14 b/lkm). Evenly distributed across all habitats except mountain and moorland with increases of 40 % in urban/suburban areas, 55 % in farmland and 71 % in coniferous woodland.

C   12 R. Devon, Alva 13 Mar. 10 Woodland Park, Alva 21 Apr and 20 Nov. 1 singing Inglewood, Alloa 20 Dec (PMA).

S   One singing Ochiltree, Dunblane 22 Jan (NB).

NUTHATCH *Sitta europaea*

Following the first record for the recording area in 1999, four more sightings were reported this year, mirroring the gradual northwards spread of this species. Presence during the breeding season is particularly encouraging with regards to future colonisation of the area.

C   Single Alva 22 Apr was in the same garden as in 1999 (PMA).

S   Single Balquhidder 22 and 25 May was photographed. 1 Dunblane 26 Aug (KE, SF).

TREECREEPER *Certhia familiaris* (B,W)

Under-recorded. Recorded in very low numbers on BBS, this year's total of 6 birds was one up on the mean of 5 (annual range: 2-8).

C   Three Cambus Pools 19 Apr (ACR).

*GREAT GREY SHRIKE *Lanius excubitor*

S   One L. Venachar 4 Apr (RR) is the 18th record for the recording area.

JAY *Garrulus glandarius* (B,W)

Recorded in very low numbers on BBS. However, this year's total of 11 birds is the highest to date (annual range: 1-11 birds with a mean of 5). Its preferred habitat is conifer woodland with 0.44 b/lkm compared to 0.07 on farmland, the only other habitat it was found in.

F   Singles Callendar Estate Woods, Falkirk 22 Jan; Bo'ness 30 Jan and 28 Dec (RDZ, RS). In breeding season 3 Dunmore Wood 24 Apr and single Torwood 15 Jun (AB).

C   In autumn/winter: singles Gartmorn Dam 9 and 25 Oct and 18 Dec; Devon Walkway, Tillicoultry 18 Nov; Alloa Bonds 28 Nov; Linn Mill 7 Dec; calling near Tulligarth Chimney 8 Dec; Aberdona Forest 29 Dec; Tait Place, Tillicoultry 31 Dec (DAC, PMA, AET, NB). In breeding season: 2 Devon Walkway, Tillicoultry 17 Apr; 2 Muckhart Mill were being mobbed by Swallows 5 May. Single The

Forest, Forestmill 21 Jun (DAC, NB, AET).

S   In autumn/winter: 5 Stronavar, L. Voil 17 Jan and 3 there 8 Dec; singles L. of Menteith 5 Feb; 3 Gart, Callander 15 Feb; Carron Valley Res. 20 Sep; Strathyre 15 Oct; G. Dochart 16 Oct; 2 Lendrick Lodge, Brig o' Turk and 3 Balquhidder both on 7 Nov; singles Argaty, Braes of Doune 8 Nov; Stonefield, Aberfoyle 13 Nov; Baad Cotts, Drip Carse 13 Nov; 2 on feeder Kaimes Fm., Stirling 18 Nov; Argaty, Braes of Doune 4 Dec; L. Watston 12 Dec (NB, DK, DAC, PWS, KS, RDZ, PAL, AB). In breeding season: single L. Voil 7 Apr; 2 Callander 10 Apr; 2 Plean CP 14 Apr; 2 S L. Tay 19 Apr; 2 Gartrenich, Flanders Moss 2 May with 1 there 8 Jun; on A81 near Callander 9 May; 3 G. Dochart 10 May; 1 Torwood 15 Jun; 2 Tom Dubh, Callander 29 Jun; 1 Cromlix Moor 4 Jul; 2 G. Dochart 28 Jul (RG, PH, PWS, GO, JM, PAL, AB, ES, DWP).

MAGPIE   *Pica pica* (B,W)

Recorded in a fairly narrow range on BBS, the 2005 rate of 0.48 b/lkm is only 4 % below the average (annual range: 0.31-0.63 b/lkm). Most numerous in urban/suburban habitat with 1.21 b/lkm compared to 0.72 in Farmland. No records received from the Airthrey roost. Continues to be very scarce NW of Dunblane. Abundant around Stirling but is not usually as frequent in the west; large groups now widespread in Falkirk

F   16 Camelon, Falkirk 21 Feb (MA).

C   Eight Longcarse, Alloa 9 Jan; 8 Tait Place, Tillicoultry 15 Jan; 8 New Sauchie 6 Feb; 12 R. Devon, Alva 27 Feb (AET, PMA).

S   Ten Lerrocks, Braes of Doune 2 Jan; 9 Hollow Burn, Fallin 24 Apr. 2 Tom Dubh, Callander 27 May and 29 Jun (MM, RHD, ES).

JACKDAW   *Corvus monedula* (B,W)

Under-recorded. The rate of 3.27 b/lkm was the highest to date, 33 % above the mean (annual range: 2.11-3.27 b/lkm). Recorded in all habitats apart from mountain and moorland with 9.22 b/lkm in urban/suburban squares, 4.82 in farmland and 0.25 in coniferous/moorland edge squares.

F   100 Skinflats 2 Nov is unusual for location (AB).

S   270-300 Argaty, Braes of Doune 20 Jan; 60 Plean CP 29 Mar with 15 there apparently building nests 16 Apr. 140 BoA 16 Nov (DAC, AB, CJH).

ROOK   *Corvus frugilegus* (B,W)

The 3rd most abundant species on BBS. The 5.25 b/lkm recorded this year is 17 % above the mean but numbers vary quite widely from year to year depending upon how many large post breeding feeding assemblages are encountered (annual range: 2.08-6.74 b/lkm).

Systematic counts of known rookeries (e.g. BoA, Gartmorn, Forth and Clyde Canal, Lake of Menteith, etc.) needed.

S   Two Ochiltree, Dunblane 12 Feb took turns to alight on smoking chimney where they raised wings to let smoke percolate (NB).

S   Small rookery at Black Boy, Stirling just about persists with 2 nests 15 Apr; only 1 nest left 2 Nov (DT).

CARRION CROW   *Corvus corone* (B,W)

The most abundant species on BBS along with Starling. The 2005 rate of 6.22 b/lkm was the highest yet, almost double the mean (annual range: 2.18-6.22 b/lkm). This year's increase was most marked on mountain/moorland habitat where a flock of c.300 birds was encountered in the Ochils. If this habitat is taken out of the equation, then numbers from the other three main habitats are up only 6 % on their combined long-term mean.

F   Flocks over 25 birds: 59 Skinflats 18 Sep with 48 there 5 Nov; 33 Bo'ness 6 Nov with 28 there 1 Dec (MVB, AS).

C 40 R. Devon, Alva 1 Dec (PMA).
S 30 Argaty, Doune 3 Feb with 32 there 13 Dec; 26 King's Park, Stirling 5 Feb; 33 Lecropt 10 Mar (ACR, MVB).

*HOODED CROW *Corvus cornix* (b, w)
No birds were recorded on this year's BBS. More records are needed to determine true status in NW of recording area.
F One Bo'ness 1 Aug is very unusual location (RS).
S In usual localities with hybrid near Brig o' Turk 22 Jan; single and hybrid Balvag Marshes 17 Jan; 25 and 11 hybrids G. Dochart 10 Jan with 9 and 7 hybrids there 7 Feb and 6 and 9 hybrids on 23 Dec; 6 and 3 hybrids L. Doine 17 Jan; 2 L. Dochart 22 Jan. 1 SE of L. Katrine 13 Oct; 1 and 1 hybrid G. Finglas 7 Nov; single Rhuveag, L. Voil 8 Dec (DAC, NB, JT, MAV). Outside usual range: hybrid Gartmore 22 Jan; 2 Flanders Moss 18 Feb were feeding on dead sheep (RHD, DWP).

*RAVEN *Corvus corax* (B,W)
Six birds were recorded on BBS in 2005, 1 more than the mean (annual range: 1-14). All records came from the mountain and moorland habitat where they were recorded at a rate of 0.19 b/lkm.
The Doune roost seems to have increased in numbers. As last year, there is an increasing number of reports from outside the core Callander-Doune-Dunblane area S to Stirling and into Clackmannanshire and Falkirk. Displaying birds over BoA may indicate that colonisation of this area is occurring.
F One Skinflats 4 Sep is unusual (JT).
C Two over Gartmorn Dam 20 Feb is unusual. 1 Dollar Glen 9 Apr; 2 Colsnaur Hill 29 May and 1 there 1 Jul (MVB, RDZ, RC).
S From core area: 60 roosted High Wood, Doune 7 Jan with 140 there 14 Feb and 60 on 2 Apr; 2 Bovain, G. Dochart 10 Jan; 1 near Brig o' Turk 22 Jan; 1 L. Mahaick 27 Jan with 4 there 25 Mar; nest Cromlix 12 Mar was destroyed by 22 Apr; 8 Lanrick Rd., Torrie 19 Mar; 10 Braes of Doune 20 Mar; 3 Balquhider 24 Apr. A pr. nested Keir Park, Dunblane. 1 NW Ochiltree, Dunblane 29 Aug; 7 above Argaty, Braes of Doune 4 Dec (DOE, DJC, NB, DAC, ACR, GO, AB). Dispersing birds were reported as follows: 3 W Carse of Lecropt 6 Feb. 6 Flanders Moss feeding on dead sheep 18 Feb with 3 flying over the moss 10 May; 1 SSE Fallin 19 Mar; up to 5 over Mine Wood, BoA on several dates in Mar, Jun, Sep and Dec. Agitated bird in Lake of Menteith heronry 19 Apr with 2 there 11 May - two birds were there 22 Apr last year. A nest was confirmed at Menteith 12 Jul. 2 Gillies Hill, Stirling 7 May. 1 Dumyat 23 Jun; 2 Carron Valley Res. 6 Sep (DT, DWP, RHD, RAB, SRS, DOE, RDZ, NT, MVB).

STARLING *Sturnus vulgaris* (B,W)
Greatly under-reported. The most abundant species, along with Carrion Crow, on BBS. This year's rate of 6.22 b/lkm is just 4 % above the mean (annual range: 4.06-10.71 b/lkm) but numbers vary greatly from year to year depending upon how many large post breeding feeding assemblages are encountered. They were only recorded in farmland, 8.51 b/lkm, and urban/suburban, 21.21 b/lkm, habitats.
F 300 Kersebrock Fm., Larbert 4 Apr. 100 Drumbowie 27 Sep with 200 there 6 Oct, 100 on 22 Nov and 200 on 21 Dec. 200 Airth 29 Oct; 150 Kincardine Bridge roost same day with 450 there 23 Dec (RHD, JS, CJH).
S 260-300 Carse of Thornhill 20 Jan; 2-300 juvs. Carse of Lecropt 30 May (DJC, ACR).

HOUSE SPARROW *Passer domesticus* (B,W)
Under-recorded. Numbers were up 17 % on the mean at 1.79 b/lkm this year. This species has a fairly narrow annual range of 1.22-2.08 b/lkm since 1997. Only

found in farmland (2.54 b/lkm) and urban/suburban (5.68 b/lkm) habitats.

F   Ca. 20 birds bred Strathavon Fm., Slamannan. Numbers there increase annually. 40 Orchardhead, Skinflats 13 Mar; 20 Falkirk 8 Oct (TF, MVB, KC).

S   110 Drum Fm., W of Kippen 19 Jan; 53 at feeding station Thornhill Carse 20 Jan. Fledgling in Ashfield garden 3 May. 30 Killin 26 Aug; 40 Lerrocks, Argaty 13 Dec (DAC, DJC, DWP, PWS, MVB).

TREE SPARROW   *Passer montanus* (B,W)
Occurs in very low numbers on BBS transects with 7 birds this year, the most to date (annual range: 0-7). All the birds were found on farmland habitat this year. An increasing number of recods seem to indicate that the species may be more widespread than in recent years.

F   Reported around ruins and cottages Skinflats on several dates Jan, Apr, May, Jul, Sep and Nov with 11 (incl. juvs.) there 14 Jul, 14 on 17 Jul, 6 on 25 Jul and 35 on 30 Sep. 10 Kersebrock Fm., Larbert 23 Jan were using wild bird cover (AB, GO, RHD). 2 at Bowtress, Airth 6 May were presumed to have bred (RHD).

C   As in 2004 reported from several locations: 4 R. Devon, Alva 3 Apr with 2 there 8 May; 10 Cambus Pools 19 Apr with 3 on track to pools 12 May. A bird carrying food Hillend Fm., Clackmannan 6 May. 4 Gartmorn Dam 25 Oct; 1 near Maggie's Wood Flood, Fishcross 5 Nov with 2 there 28 Nov. 11 Linn Mill 7 Dec (PMA, ACR, SRS, NB, AET).

S   18 Whirrieston feeding station, Thornhill 16 Jan with 40 there 24 Jan. 40 South Mid Frew feeding station, Thornhill 16 Jan with 24 there 20 Jan. 10 Frew, Thornhill Carse 9 Feb (RHD, DK, DJC, DOE). 12 Drum Fm., Kippen 19 Jan with 4 there 3 Mar and 10 Littleward Fm., Kippen 21 Jan. 10 Carse of Lecropt 15 Feb with 19 there 10 Mar. 2 ads. and 2 juvs. on the carse 19 Jun with 35 on 28 Jul and 14 on 4 Oct (DAC, MVB, DT). 8 Bandeath 5 Feb; 6 Sauchenford, Plean 6 Feb with 8 there 14 Apr. At least 14 Westhaugh, Stirling 14 Mar (RHD, RS, HS). 12 Fallin 26 Mar with a juv. there 31 May. 30 Kaimes Fm., Stirling 10 Nov where believed nesting took place. 12 Rossburn Lane, Blairdrummond 3 Dec. (PAL, MVB, RG, RHD). Smaller numbers also reported during breeding season from Bolfornought, Forthbank; Hilton Fm. Cottage, Cowie; South Kirklane, Blairdrummond Moss; Cambusbarron and Lower Greenyards, Bannockburn (RHD, RS, CS, DT).

CHAFFINCH   *Fringilla coelebs* (B,W)
Numbers increased to 4.58 b/lkm, some 10 % above the mean (annual range: 3.46-5.15 b/lkm). Numbers were highest in conifer woodland and its moorland edge at 9.19 b/lkm, followed by 5.81 in farmland and 4.48 in urban/suburban areas with even a few birds being recorded from mountain and moorland squares.

S   30 Lerrocks, Argaty 2 Jan with 550 there 5 Oct, 600 on 27 Oct, 680 on 10 Nov, 900 on 2 Dec and 620 on 13 Dec (MM, MVB) 120 Lecropt 15 Jan; 250 Argaty, Braes of Doune with 570 there 5 Nov (MVB, DOE). 1 singing Gartincaber Pond, Thornhill 24 Jan. At least 550 Gartmore 7 Apr (NB, DJC).

*BRAMBLING   *Fringilla montifringilla* (W)
F   M Camelon, Falkirk 20 Mar (MA).
C   One W Longcarse, Alloa 15 Oct (MVB).
S   65 Kinbuck, Dunblane 12 Feb; 4 King's Park, Stirling 14 Feb; 4 males/1 female Strathyre 6 May. 15 Doune 15 Oct; singles Lerrocks, Argaty 27 Oct and 10 Nov; 20 Argaty, Doune 5 Nov; single Ochiltree, Dunblane 20 and 22 Dec (MVB, ACR, DJC, DOE, NB).

GREENFINCH   *Carduelis chloris* (B,W)
Under-recorded. No very large flocks reported this year. This year's BBS rate of

1.07 b/lkm was the highest yet, up 45 % on the mean (annual range: 0.42-1.07 b/lkm). This species favours urban/suburban habitats occurring at 4.66 b/lkm here compared to 1.23 b/lkm on farmland.

F   18 Bo'ness garden 3 Mar; 55 South Alloa 15 Oct (AS, MVB).

C   37 Tullibody Inch 5 Nov (AET).

S   20 King's Park, Stirling 11 Jul with 26 there 17 Jul; 150 Argaty 5 Oct; 20 Lerrocks 27 Oct (ACR, MVB).

GOLDFINCH *Carduelis carduelis* (B,W)

Numbers on BBS were down slightly on last year but at 0.37 b/lkm still up by 32 % on the mean (annual range 0.12-0.4 b/lkm). Found at greatest density in farmland, 0.64 b/lkm but also at 0.31 b/lkm in coniferous woodland and its moorland edge.

Again no significant flocks from the Doune-Dunblane area.

F   Small flocks reported from several dates in Sep, Oct and Nov with maxima of 28 on 4 Oct and 29 on 12 Oct. 40 Kincardine Bridge 6 Nov with 120 there 3 Dec (KC, MVB).

C   39 near Tullibody Inch 20 Oct included many juvs. (AET).

S   75 Lecropt 15 Jan. Small flocks King's Park, Stirling Jun to Aug with maximum of 40 on 15 Aug. 25 Doune 8 Oct (MVB, ACR).

SISKIN *Carduelis spinus* (B,W)

Recorded almost exclusively in coniferous woodland on BBS at 1.81 b/lkm, the overall rate of 0.28 is 23 % down on the mean (annual range: 0.1-0.75 b/lkm).

F   43 West Mains Pond, Falkirk 15 Jan (MA).

C   40 Law Hill, Dollar 27 Oct (DT).

S   55 Lecropt 15 Jan; 90 Gart 5 Feb with 33 there 27 Nov (MVB). In breeding season recorded from Killin, L. Ard. G. Lochay and Balquhidder (PWS, RC, GC, RT, CJH). 45 Carse of Lecropt 18 Dec; 40 Strathyre 27 Dec (DT, DJC).

LINNET *Carduelis cannabina* (B,W)

Only 5 birds were recorded on BBS, the lowest to date (annual range: 5-35 birds). This is only 19 % of the mean. Numbers on BBS have declined over the past 3 years being down 56 % when compared with the previous 5 years when numbers were very stable. Numbers locally were highest in coniferous woodland and its moorland edge.

There continue to be fewer birds than previously in the Doune area but medium-sized flocks were again present in the Dunblane area. Smaller flocks than in previous years were reported from the Carse of Lecropt.

F   100 Bridgend Fm., Letham, Airth 19 Feb. 40 Dunmore 27 Oct; 35 Kersebrock Fm., Larbert 29 Oct. 300 Skinflats 28 Oct with 250 at Orchardhead, Skinflats 6 Nov. 35 Kinneil 4 Dec (RHD, MVB, DT).

C   250 Newrowhead, Dollar 3 Dec (DT).

S   300 Lerrocks Fm., Braes of Doune 2 Jan; at least 190 in wild bird cover at Argaty, Braes of Doune 13 Jan with at least 300 there 23 Jan; 95 Lecropt 15 Jan; 39 Robertson's Lane, Blairdrummond 29 Jan. 30 Argaty, Braes of Doune 3 Feb; 50 East Lundie 12 Feb; 150 Milton of Cambus, Braes of Doune 25 Mar; 30 Whirriestoun feeding station, Thornhill 15 Apr (MM, MVB, DK, ACR, NB). 27 Carron Valley Res. 6 Sep; 140 Pisgah, Dunblane 2 Oct with 120 there 8 Oct; 70 Stonehill, Dunblane 8 Oct; 150 Argaty, Doune 8 Oct with 110 there 14 Oct and 60 on 5 Nov; 50 W Culmore, Thornhill Carse 13 Oct; 120 Lecropt 9 Nov (NT, MVB, RHD, SZ).

TWITE *Carduelis flavirostris* (b,W)

No birds were recorded on BBS this year.

F   20 Kinneil saltmarsh 4 Jan; 70 Airth 29 Oct; 40 Kincardine Bridge and 90

Orchardhead, Skinflats 6 Nov; 55 Carron saltmarsh, Skinflats 3 Dec (RDZ, DT, MVB).

S   100 Argaty, Braes of Doune 4 Jan with 100 there 6 Feb and 3 on 5 Nov (DOE, MVB). 190 Lerrocks, Argaty 18 Feb; 27 Stonehill, Dunblane 19 Feb, with 65 there 9 Mar. 95 Kippenrait, Dunblane 19 Feb with 140 there 12 Mar (MVB). 7 singing Hollow Burn, Fallin 24 Apr were migrants (RHD). 3, including 1 singing bird, G. Dochart 14 May. AOT Braeleny, Callander 11 May (RHD, DJC). 5 SW L. Katrine 13 Oct (MAV).

LESSER REDPOLL   *Carduelis cabaret* (b,W)

Recorded in low numbers on BBS with 12 birds this year, up on the mean of 8 (annual range: 2-27).

C   35 Gartmorn 7 Dec (PMA).

S   32 Ochiltree, Dunblane 13 Jan; 70 Pier Road, Killin (NB). During breeding season reported from Drumloist, Kilbryde and Doune Lodge, Braes of Doune; Cromlix, Dunblane; Carron Valley (DOE, RG). 20 G. Lochay 23 Nov; 30 Stronvar, L. Voil 8 Dec (PWS, NB).

*COMMON CROSSBILL   *Loxia curvirostra* (b,W)

Occurs in very low numbers on BBS transects with only 4 birds recorded this year, 2 below the mean (annual range 0-11). Found only in coniferous woodland at a rate of 0.3 b/lkm.

F   Male and 4 females Oakbank Wood, Larbert 18 Nov (MA).

S   Two prs. Drymen Road, L. Ard Forest 22 Jan; 2 females nr. Brig o' Turk 22 Jan with 27 there 24 Jul. Pr. Drumloist, Braes of Doune 26 Mar; 3 Kinlochard 2 Apr; 2 Carron Valley Res. 11 Apr; 4 Gartrenich, Flanders Moss 2 May; 18 in family groups Carron Valley 30 May. Single Argaty, Braes of Doune 21 Jun with 4 there 6 Aug and 10 on 12 Nov; pr. with b/2 Bows, Braes of Doune 3 Jul. 8 Cromlix, Dunblane 6 Jul; 10 High Woods, Doune 24 Jul; 2 Strathyre 27 Jul; 9 Gart 27 Nov (RHD, DAC, DOE, JT, JM, DT, MVB).

COMMON ROSEFINCH   *Carpodacus erythrinus*

S   Male (possibly more than one bird) singing Strathyre on several dates in July. Discoverer wishes to stay unacknowledged. Photographs supplied by MMy and identification checked by local rarities committee. This is the fourth record for the recording area with previous records from 1997, 1998 and 2002.

BULLFINCH   *Pyrrhula pyrrhula* (B,W)

Occurs in low numbers on BBS with 6 birds, the same as the mean (annual range: 1-13). It occurs at similar rates in both coniferous woodland and farmland.

F   Single Bo'ness garden 14 Jan; M Torwood 15 Jun; 1 Skinflats 7 and 23 Nov (BTO, GO).

C   Six Muckhart Mill 15 Mar with 2 there feeding on Gean 5 May; 2 Cowden Fm. 2 May feeding on Gean; 4 Ms and 4 Fs feeding on docks Gartmorn Dam 24 Dec (NB, AET).

S   18 Flanders Moss 14 Jan; 11 Easter Row 3 Feb; 2 prs. Plean CP 22 Mar; 8 Kinbuck, Dunblane 1 Oct; 7 Lerrocks, Braes of Doune 7 Dec; 3 Westleys, Carse of Lecropt 18 Dec (DWP, AB, NB, MVB, DT). In breeding season 5 Thornhill 7 Apr; 2 Gartrenich, Flanders Moss 8 Jun; bird feeding Y Ardeonaig, L. Tay 24 Jun; single Argaty, Braes of Doune 4 Jul (DJC, JM, PWS, DOE).

The influx of Northern Bullfinches (*P.p. pyrrhula*) from 2004 was still apparent with 4 (2 males, 2 females) Doune 3 Feb with a male there 16 Jan and 4 birds on 22 Jan; 8 Argaty, Braes of Doune 21 Feb (DOE).

*SNOW BUNTING   *Plectrophenax nivalis* (W)

S   Five Stuc a Chroin 3 Jan; 15 Severie, Braes of Doune 14 Feb (DWP, DOE).

YELLOWHAMMER *Emberiza citrinella* (B,W)
Numbers were up by 36 % on the mean at 0.49 b/lkm (annual range: 0.08-0.61 b/lkm) with all the birds being recorded on farmland.
F   19 Higgins Neuk 19 Jan. At least 20 Kersebrock Fm., Larbert were using wild bird cover 23 Jan with 25 there 5 Feb and 20 on 19 Feb (MVB, RHD).
S   45 Lecropt 15 Jan with 33 there 15 Feb, 14 on 20 Feb, 19 on 10 Mar, 13 on 4 Oct and 10 on 19 Nov (MVB, DK). 12 South Mid Frew feeding station, Thornhill 16 Jan with 30 there 9 Feb; 42 at Whirrieston feeding station, Thornhill 11 Feb. 30 Howietoun, W of Stirling 20 Jan; 31 Thornhill Carse 20 Jan; 20 Rossburn Lane, Blairdrummond 3 Dec (DK, DOE, DJC, MVB).

REED BUNTING *Emberiza schoeniclus* (B,W)
Numbers fell to their lowest level yet with only 11 birds recorded, down 47 % on the mean (annual range 11-35 birds). It was recorded at its highest levels on mountain and moorland squares.
F   At least 25 in wild bird cover Kersebrock Fm., Larbert 8 Jan with at least 50 there 23 Jan; 40 on 5 Feb and 100 on 19 Feb. 14 by R. Carron, Skinflats 9 Jan; 5 South Alloa 4 Apr; 10 South Alloa 27 Oct; 8 Blackness 6 Nov (RHD, MVB, AS).
C   Seven Alloa Inches 7 Feb. In breeding season at Cambus Pools; Blackgrange, Cambus; Gartmorn Dam and Woodland Park, Alva (AET, ACR, PMA, DRO).
S   20 Littleward Fm., Poldar Moss 21 Jan; 9 Drymen Road, L. Ard Forest 22 Jan; 13 Lecropt 13 Mar; 10 Lerrocks, Argaty 27 Oct (DAC, RHD, MVB). In breeding season reported from Carron Valley where a pair was building a nest 30 May; Hollow Burn, Fallin; Lecropt and L. Tay, Killin (RHD).

ESCAPED SPECIES

SNOW GOOSE *Anser caerulescens*
S   Long-staying blue-phase bird still present all year round at North Third Res. (BO).
BARNACLE GOOSE *Branta leucopsis*
S   One R. Forth (no detailed location given) with 23 Canada Geese 25 Oct. The long-staying bird from North Third Res. was last seen in Nov (PAL, BO).
MUSCOVY DUCK *Cairina moschata*
C   One Gartmorn Dam 17 Feb (ACR).
S   Two Doune Pond 30 Jan (NDW).
EGYPTIAN GOOSE *Alopochen aegyptiacus*
This is probably the bird that has been on the Forth since 22 Jan 2003 when it was first noted at Skinflats. It was seen till at least early August.
F   Kinneil 3 Aug with moulting Shelduck (MVB).
C   Blackgrange, Cambus 29 Jan; Midtown, Cambus 12 Feb; Cambus Pools 10 and 19 Apr and 3 Jun; Cambus Village Pools 24 Apr and 3 Jul (RHD, AET, PMA, ACR).
MANDARIN DUCK *Aix galericulata*
S   Female Plean CP 15 Apr could have been one of the birds from last year. Pr. Cambusmore/Gart GP 28 May. F there 22 and 28 Jun (GO, NB, DT).
WOOD DUCK *Aix sponsa*
The male from last year still present, possibly all year round.
S   Castle Business Pk., Stirling 5, 9 and 21 Jan; 20 Feb; 1 Nov; 17, 20 and 28 Dec (RS, BNS, NB).
RED-LEGGED PARTRIDGE *Alectoris rufa*
S   Five Dykehead, Lake of Menteith 28 Jan (DAC).

WEATHER 2005 PARKHEAD CLIMATOLOGICAL STATION

Malcolm G. Shaw

Introduction A new automatic digital system was added to the Parkhead Climatological Station, Stirling University at the end of 2004. The recording system now records much more continuous information. For example mean daily temperatures/rain falls/wind strengths from hourly readings are now possible along with the maxima and minima and the hour of day at which they were recorded. For this year data has been extracted which allows direct comparison with the 30 year Climatological Normals (CNs) established in 2000 (1771-2000). For the future, as data is accumulated, it should be possible to offer a fuller comparison of local weather variations.

The bad news is that due to some unwanted attention the Station suffered damage and the loss of the January data. In order to allow some general annual comparisons to be made still, the yearly CNs published in Volume 24 of the Forth Naturalist have been recalculated on an 11 month basis by subtracting the measurements and means for January. Where appropriate these replace the CNs (in brackets) following this year's figures in Tables 1 and 2.

The year 2005 (Jan-Dec). Taken as a whole the year was slightly warmer (mean temp. maxima +0.4°C mean temp. minima +0.9°C) and wetter (+58 mm, 7 %). What stands out though is that whilst the higher temperature maxima/minima were common to all months except November and December which were close to average, the rain was concentrated in the spring (April-June) and the month of October. These months together received no less than 57 % of an average annual fall (475 mm vs 832 mm) and more than double the CNs for these months.

The summer and late autumn were then comparatively dry.

February – March The first half of February continued mild as had been in much of January, as some may recall. Until the 13th there were no air frosts and day time highs reached 10°C. 85 % of the month's rain fell. Winds were mostly from the west and though no gales, gusts of 13-43 kph were recorded every day. A good month for windmills you might think.

In the second half of the month, the winds veered to the north, backed and veered again settling in the north and east until mid March. Snow was seen in the air in the third week of February and again some settled during the first two weeks of March. When it wasn't windy, and most days were, an average number of air frosts were recorded.

From the third week of March milder air was associated with a series of depressions, wind and average rain from every quarter, but with some good highs of 15°C and nights little cooler at (11°C).

April – June. These three months were characterised by the same wet mild windy unsettled weather, as late March. Grass grows well in these conditions, I am informed, but at the same time further south in the UK, almost annual, preparations were being made for a hosepipe ban.

There were no air frosts (last on 14th March), though an average of 5 plus are noted in the CNs. Otherwise temperature minima were unexceptional, given the cloudy days, and wind. Day time highs were also unexceptional, but mid June recorded 12 days with temperatures of 20-24°C, light winds with near average rain. June was still ranked as the 5th wettest month of the year.

July, August and September   July, especially 2nd and 3rd weeks might be remembered as one of the warmest and driest for some years. Day temperature maxima were well up 20-29°C and light rain on only 7 days. August and September had near average rain fall with above average temperature maxima and minima.

Winds were generally light from the WSW though depressions in late August and September produce gusts of up to 41 kph (ca. 23kts).

October was one of the wettest months on record. In other years, without having had some respite in late summer there would have been serious fears for the harvest. In the second week alone 73 mm of rain were recorded. As might be expected, temperature highs and especially lows were above average and again no air frosts were recorded. Winds too were unexceptional for October.

November   The first two weeks seemed to continued the pattern of October, with moderate winds, above average rain and no frosts.

From the 16th temperatures fell and every second night had a serious frost. On the 18th Parkhead CS recorded its lowest minimum night temperature for the year of –4.8°C and its first negative mean daily temperature. It was to record another four "negative" days before the year end. Snow began to appear on the hills.

December Temperatures in the month were very close to average. Precipitation was actually very low although December normally is the wettest month of the year. In 2005 it was the second driest. It was also one of the quietest months, having four windless days and matching June for the lowest mean wind strength (1.4 kph, <1kt).

The hopes of a white Christmas were not realised, but snow, at least above 50 m, was delivered to most areas in Christmas week.

Table 1 Temperature readings Parkhead Climatological Station
February to December 2005

	mean - maxima		mean - minima		Number of Air Frosts	
February	7.4	(6.9)*	1.6	(0.8)*	9	(11)*
March	10.2	(9.1)	4.0	(1.9)	8	(7)
April	11.8	(11.8)	4.2	(3.4)	0	(4)
May	14.9	(15.3)	5.4	(5.8)	0	(1)
June	18.5	(17.7)	10.7	(8.4)	0	(<1)
July	20.1	(19.8)	11.3	(10.6)	0	(0)
August	20.0	(19.4)	10.4	(10.2)	0	(0)
September	17	(16.3)	9.5	(8.3)	0	(<1)
October	13.8	(12.9)	8.3	(5.4)	0	(2)
November	8.8	(9.2)	2.1	(2.6)	11	(8)
December	7.2	(7.2)	1.2	(1.1)	14	(11)
Year February-December 2005	13.6	(13.2)	6.2	(5.3)	42	(44)

* Climatological Normals 1971-2000 are shown in brackets.

Table 2 Rainfall and Wind Feb.-Dec. 2005 Parkhead Climatological Station

	Total rain (mm)		Greatest fall (mm)		Number of days >0.2 mm		Number of days >1.0 mm		Number of days >5 mm		mean Wind strength (m/s)	Gust max. at time, date (m/s)
February	50.8	(73.2)*	13.0	(31.8)*	15	(16)	9	(12)	3	(5)	0.8 .	12.1 SW 13.00, 13/02
March	75.4	(81.4)	15.2	(44.0)	18	(17)	15	(14)	4	(5)	0.7 .	11.2 SW 09.00, 16/03
April	98.6	(47.5)	27.1	(35.3)	17	(13)	11	(10)	6	(3)	0.9 .	14.8 WSW** 11.00, 15/04
May	116.1	(56.9)	23.6	(28.3)	17	(14)	14	(11)	7	(4)	0.9 .	13.4 ENE 00.00, 27/05
June	86.4	(57.1)	15.5	(35.8)	16	(13)	13	(10)	4	(4)	0.4 .	8.5 N 13.00, 12/06
July	15.0	(62.9)	4.2	(65.5)	10	(13)	5	(10)	0	(5)	0.6 .	9.8 ENE 11.00, 29/07
August	68.8	(68.1)	14.2	(30.0)	20	(14)	14	(11)	4	(5)	0.5 .	11.2 WSW 17.00, 24/08
September	69.6	(87.7)	21.3	(44.2)	15	(15)	13	(12)	4	(6)	0.6 .	11.6 WSW 16.00, 23/09
October	174.0	(97.9)	42.4**	(66.2)	19	(17)	17	(14)	11	(6)	0.5 .	11.6 E 11.00, 24/10
November	88.1	(98.9)	18.5	(68.3)	20	(17)	12	(14)	6	(7)	0.6 .	12.5 SW 15.00, 11/11
December	48.3	(101.0)	9.9	(43.8)	21	(18)	10	(15)	3	(7)	0.4 .	9.4 N 21.00, 15/12
Year Feb.-Dec. 2005	891.1	(832.3)	42.4**	(68.3)	188	(167)	133	(133)	52	(57)	0.6 .	14.8 WSW **

* Climatological normals 1971-2000 are shown in brackets.